Field Studies, **9**, (1997) 179 - 269

A KEY TO THE ADULTS OF BRIT
AND THEIR ALLI
(NEUROPTERA, MEGALOPTERA, RA. ....
MECOPTERA)

Colin W. Plant

14 West Road, Bishops Stortford, Hertfordshire CM23 3QP

ABSTRACT

The British Neuropterida consists of 73 species comprising four Raphidioptera, three megalopters and 66 Neuroptera. Though not closely related, the four British species of Mecoptera have traditionally been studies with the Neuropterida. Existing identification works are, to an extent, unreliable and the addition of several species to the British fauna in recent years has in any case rendered them incomplete. This AIDGAP guide includes illustrated keys to all currently known British Isles species of Neuropterida and Mecoptera and provides some notes on each species.

CONTENTS

INTRODUCTION

Lacewings (Neuroptera), alder flies (Megaloptera), snake flies (Raphidioptera) and scorpion flies (Mecoptera) together form a relatively small portion of the British insect fauna, numbering only 77 species in total. Traditionally, they have been treated together in several key works, such as the Royal Entomological Society's *Handbooks for the Identification of British Insects*, though in reality the Mecoptera are not that closely related to the other three groups.

The purpose of this paper is to present new and up-to-date identification keys for the British Neuroptera, Megaloptera, Raphidioptera and Mecoptera.

Most entomologists agree that British lacewings may be categorised as follows:

> ORDER MEGALOPTERA – *the alder flies*
>   (1 genus: 3 species)
> ORDER RAPHIDIOPTERA – *the snake flies*
>   (1 genus: 4 subgenera, 4 species)
> ORDER NEUROPTERA – *the true lacewings*
>   (22 genera: 66 species)

together with
> ORDER MECOPTERA – the scorpion flies
>   (2 genera, 4 species)

This higher taxonomy is adopted in the keys which follow.

There has been a great deal of confusion over the names of the British lacewings. This is discussed briefly in Appendix 4. The major changes in names are summarised in Table 1, whilst the additions to the British and Irish list are given in Table 2. As a further guide, the reader is referred to the notes on each species included after the keys, in Appendix 1. A fully synonymic checklist can be found in Plant (1994), where both generic and specific synonyms are listed in full (but see Table 1 for changes).

Distribution

Our knowledge of the distribution of British lacewings and allies has been expanded considerably during the past nine years, since the National Recording Scheme for lacewings and allies was launched in 1988 and comments in Fraser (1959) and Killington (1936, 1937) on the subject should be disregarded. The contributions by amateur and professional entomologists to this scheme have culminated in the publication by the Institute of Terrestrial Ecology's Biological Records Centre of the *Provisional Atlas of the Neuroptera, Megaloptera, Raphidioptera and Mecoptera of the British Isles* (Plant, 1994). As a guide to which species may be expected in which geographical area, the national distributions are broadly summarised in the species notes in Appendix 1 of this paper. It should be emphasised, however, that the distribution data is provisional and that there are large areas of Britain that are poorly recorded or not recorded at all for lacewings; this is particularly true for Scotland and Ireland. Whilst the presence of a particular species in a new area should not be greeted with unnecessary surprise, therefore, the author would nevertheless be pleased to confirm identifications of species that are apparently out of range.

TABLE 1: *Principal name changes made to British lacewings since publication of the keys by Fraser in 1959*

Old name	Source	Current name
ORDER NEUROPTERA		
Aleuropteryx lutea	Fraser, 1959	*Helicoconis lutea* *
Anisochrysa spp.	Aspöck et al, 1980	*Dichochrysa* spp.
Boriomyia mortoni	Killington, 1937	*Wesmaelius malladai*
Chrysopa carnea	Fraser, 1959	*Chrysoperla carnea*
Chrysopa flava	Fraser, 1959	*Nineta flava*
Chrysopa flavifrons	Fraser, 1959	*Dichochrysa flavifrons*
Chrysopa septempunctata	Fraser, 1959	*Chrysopa pallens*
Chrysopa ciliata	Fraser, 1959	*Chrysopidia ciliata*
Chrysopa albolineata	Fraser, 1959	*Cunctochrysa albolineata*
Chrysopa vittata	Fraser, 1959	*Nineta vittata*
Chrysopa ventralis	Fraser, 1959	*Dichochrysa prasina*
Chrysopa ventralis ssp. *prasina*	Fraser, 1959	
	Killington, 1936	*Dichochrysa prasina*
Coniopteryx parthenia	Plant, 1994	*Coniopteryx pygmaea* **
Conwentzia psociformis form *pineticola*	Fraser, 1959	*Conwentzia pineticola*
Kimminsia baltica	Fraser, 1959	*Wesmaelius balticus*
Kimminsia killingtoni	Fraser, 1959	*Wesmaelius malladai*
Kimminsia rava	Fraser, 1959	*Wesmaelius ravus*
Kimminsia subnebulosa	Fraser, 1959	*Wesmaelius subnebulosus*
Mallada flavifrons	Plant, 1994	*Dichochrysa flavifrons*
Mallada prasina	Plant, 1994	*Dichochrysa prasina*
Mallada ventralis	Plant, 1994	*Dichochrysa ventralis*
Nathanica capitata	Fraser, 1959	*Nothochrysa capitata*
Nathanica fulviceps	Fraser, 1959	*Nothochrysa fulviceps*
ORDER RAPHIDIOPTERA		
Raphidia cognata	Fraser, 1959	*Subilla confinis*
Raphidia maculicollis	*Fraser, 1959*	*Atlantoraphidia maculicollis*
Raphidia notata	*Fraser, 1959*	*Phaeostigma notata*
Raphidia xanthostigma	*Fraser, 1959*	*Xanthostigma xanthostigma*

* *Helicoconis lutea* is no longer regarded as a valid British species (see Plant, 1991, 1994).
** Some further comments on the name of *Coniopteryx pygmaea* are given in the notes on page 252.

Identification

The main problem that has beset the study of lacewings and their allies in Britain over the last thirty years has been the lack of adequate, English-language identification keys. The last such work was published as far back as 1959 in the Royal Entomological Society's *Handbooks for the Identification of British Insects series* (Fraser, 1959), and is inevitably now out of date. In addition, a number of errors plague that work, most notably the reversal of several couplets.

TABLE 2: *Species of lacewing recorded in Britain since the publication of Fraser's key by the Royal Entomological Society in 1959*

Species	Literature reference	Comments
MEGALOPTERA		
SIALIDAE		
Sialis nigripes	Barnard, 1977	Overlooked resident
NEUROPTERA		
CONIOPTERYGIDAE		
Coniopteryx esbenpeterseni	Hynd & Plant, 1991	Overlooked resident
Coniopteryx lentiae	Hynd, 1989	Overlooked resident
Helicoconis sp. *?hirtinervis*	unpublished record	Overlooked resident?
Semidalis pseudouncinata	Plant, 1992	Recent colonist
HEMEROBIIDAE		
Hemerobius fenestratus	Plant & Barnard, 1988	Probable recent colonist
CHRYSOPIDAE		
Chrysopa commata	Barnard, 1978	Overlooked resident
Cunctochrysa bellifontensis	Plant, 1993	Status uncertain
Nineta inpunctata	Plant, 1996	Status uncertain
MYRMELEONTIDAE		
Euroleon nostras	Mendel, 1996	Overlooked resident

Authorities for these names are given in the notes section in Appendix 1, page 248.

Excellent keys for all the European species of Neuroptera, Megaloptera and Raphidioptera are currently available. The most valuable are those by Aspöck *et al.* (1980) which include genitalia drawings of most species and wing photographs of all. They are particularly useful in terms of being aware of potential new species colonising Britain, as appears to be the case with *Semidalis pseudouncinata* and *Hemerobius fenestratus*, and of species which have been residents for longer periods but whose presence may still remain undetected, as was the case with *Coniopteryx esbenpeterseni* and *C. lentiae*. However, there are two major drawbacks to the use of this two-volume work: first, it is in German, a language which sadly few British people can understand, and, secondly, it costs in the region of £240! Unfortunately, at the time of writing, there does not appear to be any adequate compilation of keys to European Mecoptera.

My aim has been, therefore, to produce usable, English language keys to the known British species of lacewings and allies, taking into account other species which may be present, but excluding those southern European and other species which are very unlikely ever to occur here.

In doing so, I have been mindful of the great many identification pitfalls communicated to me over the past few years in my role as co-ordinator of the national recording scheme. The venation in particular of most lacewings is extremely variable and there are few venational characters which can be used reliably; many insects will have different venation on left and right sides of their bodies! However, there are several occasions where, whilst not all examples of a particular species possess a particular character, the possession of that character is not shared by other species. Thus a given single species may present 'easy' and 'difficult' specimens for identification. I have therefore allowed a few species to key out more than once in the same key and, though this may appear to make the keys longer than is absolutely necessary, it should, hopefully, avoid misidentifications of common species with atypical characters.

I have also tried to simplify key characters by illustrating them with a drawing wherever possible. Complicated, or hard to see-characters are deliberately avoided if there is a simpler way of separating species, or else they are included after other characters for confirmation only. A good example would be the four British species of *Sympherobius*. In the past, successful identification of these has relied on preparing the male genitalia and consigning females to a waste bin of unidentifiable specimens. One is led to the inevitable conclusion that earlier keys were based on few specimens, since my own experience of examining literally thousands of specimens in museums, private collections and from the Rothamsted Insect Survey light trap network shows that both sexes of the four British species can be separated very easily using wing characters and a low power binocular microscope. Genitalia drawings of the males are added for confirmation only, and attention is drawn to an additional European species which may occur here. Similarly, the earlier British keys have given no indication that female *Wesmaelius* can be separated; this is simply not true, since all have quite distinctively different anal plate arrangements and these can be seen by simply placing the detached abdomen in some hot potassium hydroxide (which may be obtained over the counter at most chemist shops) for about half an hour and examining under a magnification as low as x20.

I have also tried to avoid such annoying couplet choices as 'insect larger or insect smaller'. These totally meaningless statements are replaced by finite measurements in millimetres. An example would be the statement in Fraser (1959) that the costal space of *Hemerobius marginatus* is 'abnormally wide'. Though it is the case that in some examples the enlarged costal space is glaringly obvious, I have frequently had to correct examples of *H. lutescens* incorrectly assigned to this species and *vice versa*. This problem is particularly evident in females, since both species have an elongated terminal segment to the abdomen. A simple means of measuring this space is presented, along with other hopefully helpful characters.

It is, however, important to state that the key characters selected for use are based on experience of species known to occur in Britain. Many of these characters could well be shared by examples of other species present in Europe. Where appropriate, at the start of each of the keys I have highlighted selected European species that could potentially occur in Britain but it should be realised at the outset that **these keys should be used for British species only**. Specimens which do not quite fit, or which have been collected on trips abroad, should be identified using the keys in Aspöck *et al.* (1980) or sent to the author for an opinion (accompanied by return postage stamps!).

Through the medium of the newsletter *Neuro News* of the Neuroptera Recording Scheme, several of the characters used in the keys have already been the subject of intensive field testing. Some earlier characters have indeed been rejected as a consequence of this. Hopefully, the AIDGAP testing procedure adopted for an earlier test version of these keys now presented will make things easier still.

Inevitably, however, problems may still occur and the author would positively welcome the opportunity to examine and return any problem specimens and at the same time invites anyone interested in participating in the National Recording Scheme to please get in touch at his address on page 179.

Recognising lacewings and their allies

Most true lacewings (Fig. 1) can be recognised instantly on sight, particularly the green lacewings that are found indoors during winter (these are almost always *Chrysoperla carnea* – our only species which hibernates as an adult). Snake flies have a distinctive pronotum from which their colloquial name is derived (Fig. 3); no other British insect has the combination of the elongate pronotum and four fully developed membranous wings. Male scorpion flies (Fig. 2) have a scorpion-like 'tail' held forward over the body (actually the genital capsule and quite lacking in a sting) and though females have 'normal' abdomens, their wing patterning is identical to that of the males which means that when one has become familiar with the former, then one is by definition also familiar with the latter. The Mecoptera as a whole are the only British insects which have the face produced downwards to form a 'beak' bearing biting mouthparts at the tip (Figs 5a, b & c). Alder flies are also relatively distinctive (Fig. 4), though confusion is possible with some stone flies (Plecoptera, Fig. 7b). All lacewings (except scorpion flies which are actually only distantly related to the other three groups) hold their wings over their body like a pitched roof or a tent. This is true in life and almost always in death, the only exceptions being the very few that die awkwardly in malaise traps or some light traps. Stoneflies hold their wings overlapped and flat on top of the abdomen in the horizontal plane. Mayflies (Ephemeroptera) usually hold their wings up like a butterfly and have two or three 'tail streamers' (Fig. 7a); these appendages are quite absent from British lacewings (though two very short ones are present in scorpion flies). Only caddis flies (Trichoptera) remain to cause confusion, as they also hold their closed wings like a tent over the body. They can be recognised by their quite different venation, stouter antennae (in most, but not all, species) and by the presence (in British species) of hairs arising from the wing membrane (all hairs on the wings of lacewings arise from the veins). In fact, freshly emerged British caddis are usually so densely hairy that it is necessary to rub the hairs off them in order to see venation. However, specimens from light traps, for example, may often be so rubbed that the wing membranes may appear hairless, so some caution is needed by inexperienced entomologists.

Special mention should be made of the wax flies (Coniopterygidae). These are rather unusual lacewings in appearance as they are all very small and in the field resemble whitefly, aphids or booklice (psocids). Recognising that many readers will indeed encounter insects of whose higher taxonomic position they are uncertain, the first of the following keys (Key A), attempts to deduce whether or not the insect under the microscope is in fact a lacewing.

Finding and catching lacewings *

Lacewings can be found in a wide variety of different habitats, from ancient broad-leaved woodlands to modern pine plantations, from farmland to urban gardens, from marram-fixed sand dunes to sparsely vegetated mountain slopes. It is no surprise, therefore, that the ways in which lacewings may best be found are equally varied.

---

* Additional information on collecting and preserving lacewings and allies is given in Appendix 2 on page 262.

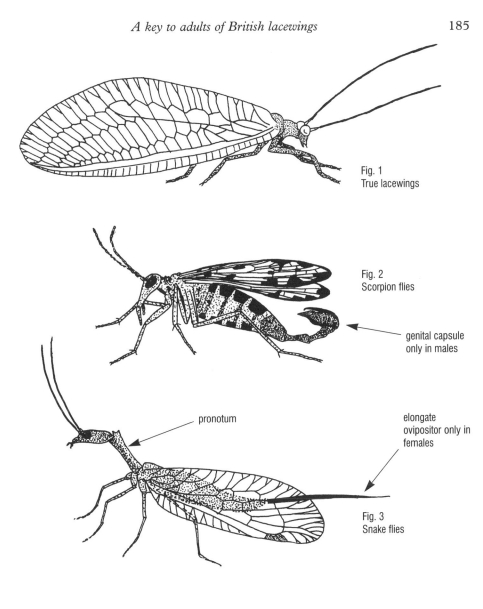

Fig. 1
True lacewings

Fig. 2
Scorpion flies

genital capsule
only in males

pronotum

elongate
ovipositor only in
females

Fig. 3
Snake flies

Fig. 4
Alder flies

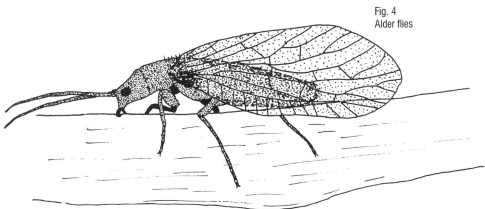

The most effective method of general sampling of the lacewings in a given area is to use a light trap, a technique which serves to emphasise the fact that all our British lacewings are either nocturnal or crepuscular (active at dawn and dusk). This may either employ a mercury vapour lamp of the type used in moth traps or a tungsten filament bulb of the type used in normal house lighting – both are equally effective, the latter perhaps slightly more so. On suitably warm evenings green lacewings (Chrysopidae) in particular may be attracted in number, together with smaller numbers of the brown species and, occasionally, scorpion flies. The most frequently recorded species is *Chrysoperla carnea* agg., closely followed by *Micromus paganus*, *Wesmaelius subnebulosus*, then *Dichochrysa flavifrons* and *Cunctochrysa albolineata*. Other species come in smaller numbers, usually, and almost all the British species have been recorded by this method at some stage.

Making friends with your local Lepidopterist could provide a good source of material and could become an effective method of surveying the lacewings of your local area, whilst simply leaving the kitchen light on and the window open during summer evenings will soon give you a reasonable garden list. Most species will rest on the ceiling and are easily collected into a tube; look carefully or you may miss the very small wax flies (Coniopterygidae) which will be camouflaged against a white ceiling!

Malaise traps too can be productive if set in a suitable position, though the prospect of sorting through the bulk of material that such a method usually gathers, in order to find specimens of wax flies, is somewhat daunting. The method is non-selective and almost any species may turn up, depending on the habitat at and near the trap site. Nevertheless it is worth mentioning that some success has been had using aerial malaise traps, set in the canopy of woodland, a technique which has helped confirm the arboreal preferences of some species (Hollier & Belshaw, 1993).

Most people, however, will prefer to use rather more traditional methods of finding lacewings, including the use of wide-bore plastic tubing and pooters for live observation. Sweep netting of vegetation from June to August can be very productive; indeed a great many specimens sent to the Recording Scheme for identification have been collected in this way by Dipterists. *Chrysopa perla*, *C. commata* and sometimes *Micromus variegatus* are often collected in this manner, along with other species from grassland habitats; the latter species is also common on hedge banks. Sweeping deciduous scrub, especially young oaks *Quercus* sp. and elms *Ulmus* sp., yields a different set of species, often including *Hemerobius lutescens* and *H. humulinus*, amongst other brown lacewings and both *Chrysopa pallens* and *Nineta vittata* amongst the greens. Beating oak scrub in particular may well turn up further examples of *Nineta inpunctata* – the latest addition to the British list. Bramble scrub with stinging nettles, though very difficult to sweep, can be the best place to find scorpion flies *Panorpa* spp. Sweeping riverside vegetation will usually yield *Sialis* species during the spring.

Beating the accessible branches of trees, including both broad-leaved and coniferous species, may also be worthwhile. However, this is best done in the earlier part of the morning; it appears that whilst some lacewings may settle on the lower branches after their nocturnal flight, the rising sun acts as a stimulus for them to fly higher. Bear in mind also that branches next to paths are less likely to yield lacewings than those further back if the path has already been disturbed by dog-walkers and other early rising competitors! Several species can be found in this way. *Atlantoraphidia maculicollis* is frequently found in the south of England at the tips of plantation pine branches during the early morning sunshine in May. Whether this is also the case in the north of England is not yet known. Larch *Larix decidua* may yield *Wesmaelius quadrifasciatus* whilst Scots pine *Pinus sylvestris* may produce *W. concinnus*, among other species, during June. The first British specimen of *Hemerobius fenestratus* was accidentally disturbed from pine branches during a September evening whilst setting up moth traps.

Many arboreal species can be collected by using a stouter than usual net on a long pole. This can either be used to sweep the higher branches of trees or else, if the bag is large enough, can be inserted over the end of a branch and shaken violently to dislodge the insects. A long-handled net was used to great effect by the late H. L. Burrows at Burnt Wood, Staffordshire, in the early 1930s when, together with R.G. Warren, he took several *Nothochrysa fulviceps* in a short space of time from the canopy of the oak trees. I have also had some success in catching *Phaeostigma notata* using a long-handled net from deer-shooting platforms erected in the lower canopy of oak trees in Essex woodlands so this may be worth trying too. Sweeping the lower level vegetation in and around woodlands immediately after unusually strong winds will sometimes turn up the odd dislodged specimen, though generally speaking the stronger winds tend to be at the wrong time of year for entomology.

However, some species may be confined to the extreme tops of very tall trees and are clearly out of the reach of the ordinary entomologist. In general, short of fogging the upper branches with insecticides there is little that can be recommended. This latter method is best reserved for serious research programmes; it can yield large numbers of lacewings of a variety of species (for example, see Barnard *et al.* 1986). On the other hand, anyone who has access to the hydraulic platforms used to repair street lights or similar machinery could easily add considerably to our knowledge by sampling the canopy of accessible trees.

It is worth noting that the behaviour of insects on disturbance varies, and a knowledge of this can help considerably in their capture for identification. *Wesmaelius concinnus*, for example, tends to drop to the ground like a falling leaf when the lower branches of pine trees are bashed with a stick. You would be surprised how long it takes the average entomologist to remember that pine trees don't have leaves! By then, the insect is lost on the ground. Scorpion flies invariably fold their wings and drop down at the slightest disturbance; they are best captured by gently inserting a small net below the insect and then disturbing the vegetation so that they literally fall into the net. Only rarely do they take to flight and escape. Most green lacewings, on the other hand, take to flight readily on disturbance and are often lost from the beating tray unless a second person is standing by with a net.

Back at ground level, simple water traps (shallow, yellow or white trays of water placed on the ground) may attract certain species, and this is the single most productive method to date for finding *Psectra diptera*, which seems plentiful in a variety of grassland habitats, from the acidic bog grasslands of the Welsh uplands to the fenland habitats of the Norfolk Broads and the short-turf chalk grasslands of the south coast. This species is also recorded occasionally from pitfall traps, a technique which can also yield the snow-flea *Boreus hyemalis* – as long as the traps are set out during the winter when the insect is active. Both *P. diptera* and *B. hyemalis* can also be found by grubbing around on the ground with your hands and collecting specimens directly into a pooter. It was using this method that the only British record of *Helicoconis sp. ? hirtinervis* was made from litter beneath heather *Calluna vulgaris* on coastal sand dunes. Searching the ground also seems to be a fairly good way of locating the three British *Micromus* species which may be feeding, as larvae, on various root aphids.

Direct searching can, in fact, be as rewarding as any other technique. Newly emerged adults of *Sialis lutaria* are easily spotted on waterside vegetation in April and May, drying their wings in the sunshine. In some areas *S. fuliginosa* and *S. nigripes* will also be present. *Sisyra* species are frequently found resting by day under bridges and under overhanging tree branches next to clean freshwater. Bridges in particular are a good place to find *Osmylus fulvicephalus* as it shelters in the cool shade by day. Examination of aphid-infested shoots of various plants will sometimes reveal adult female *Hemerobius* species in the act of egg-laying. Examination of Scots pine trunks, in early morning sunshine during May, might yield newly emerged adults of *Wesmaelius ravus* walking up to the tree top.

Suction-sampling can be a very useful technique in grassland habitats. Provisional results show the average density of lacewings in grassland to be similar to that of carabid and staphylinid beetles – ground and rove beetles respectively – suggesting that the ecological significance of lacewings in this habitat has been under-estimated.

Studying lacewing ecology

Naming your lacewing is the first, very important step in the study of this fascinating group of insects. The next is to send in the information relating to the capture to the Lacewing Recording Scheme (to me at the address on page 179). This helps our understanding of lacewing ecology in several ways. First, it adds to our knowledge of distribution. Knowledge of the geographical distribution of an insect species is fundamental to later understanding of other aspects of the insect's ecology. From such information we learn, for example, that *Chrysopa abbreviata* and *Wesmaelius balticus* are strictly confined to coastal areas (see Plant, 1994). This allows for the later research that demonstrates that sand dunes with marram grass are a strict ecological requirement for the survival of these species. Similarly, we discover that *Megalomus hirtus* requires wood sage *Teucrium scorodonia* on rocky, exposed slopes and that it is now confined apparently to a single British locality. We can now target areas to search for new localities. Next, after distribution, your record gives information on phenology (flight period) and voltinism (number of generations in a single year). Put with all the other single records sent in a similar manner, analysis of dates is possible and some pretty interesting results are generated. Monitoring shifts in flight periods may also be an effective means of monitoring certain areas of environmental change, most particularly climatic changes. There is also some information which suggests that lacewings in Scotland emerge and fly up to two weeks later than in southern England.

All this has come from identifying a single lacewing specimen. But there are many more aspects of lacewing ecology that anyone can study, usually without any need to kill any specimens (though it is vital that you are sure of the identification of the population you are studying). The larvae of a great many species have not been adequately described from British material, for example, and for some species the larva has not been described at all, nor do we even know how many eggs the females of all species lay. No reliable key to larvae exists at present. Little is truly known about the feeding habits and preferences of the larvae of several species. Most green lacewings prey on aphids, as do most of the browns. But which aphids? *Micromus* sp. for example may prefer root aphids whilst the larvae of *Hemerobius pini* are regularly recorded feeding on various pine aphids. *Psectra diptera* may be associated as an adult with grass tussocks, but it is not known where the larvae can be located nor what they feed on – the only recent records are from DVac suction samples from grassland. Larvae of snake flies are predators of beetle larvae under loose bark, possibly also of Diptera larvae; very little is written on which species of snake fly eats which beetle larva. There must be differences or why else would *A. maculicollis* be restricted to pine trees whilst the other three species evidently prefer deciduous ones. These larvae are extremely easy to find. Great contributions to our knowledge could be made by studying wild larvae, observing their natural diet (many insect larvae in captivity will eat a variety of foods that they would not normally take in the wild), their predators, their parasites and so on. Identification should always be confirmed by rearing adults from such larvae. Published descriptions of British lacewing larvae, and a key for their separation, are long overdue in the entomological literature.

Another major area of weakness in our knowledge of lacewing ecology in Britain is that of plant and habitat associations. Unfortunately, several statements in the older entomological literature contain assumptions which have since been proved to be incorrect. A record of a lacewing taken from an oak tree, for example, may have been used as the basis of a statement that the species is found on oak trees. True, it has been – once! No mention is made of the fact that the oak tree stands amongst a group of pine trees. The insect is, in fact, strictly confined to pines, and was only by chance resting on an adjacent tree.

Such a misinterpretation of data has been fairly typical in the past study of British Neuroptera. This has been compounded by accurate data based on dubiously identified species. The sad fact is that we know remarkably little of the insect-plant associations, or even in some cases the overall habitat requirements, of lacewings in the British Isles. This puts us some way behind continental European entomologists who have sorted out the answers to most of these questions. What is true in Europe may be true in Britain, but we have yet to prove it for most species.

The known or supposed habitat and plant associations in this country are shown in Table 3.

TABLE 3: *Apparent habitat preferences of species of lacewings, scorpion flies and their allies in Britain*

SPECIES APPARENTLY CONFINED TO WOODLAND HABITATS

1: Species apparently associated with coniferous trees
  Atlantoraphidia maculicollis pine and larch recorded
  Hemerobius atrifrons confined to larch?
  H. contumax confined to Scots pine? possibly extinct in Britain
  Wesmaelius concinnus confined to Scots pine?
  W. quadrifasciatus confined to larch?
  Chrysopa dorsalis confined to Scots pine?

2. Species apparently confined to oak trees
  Phaeostigma notata
  Nineta flava
  N. vittata
  Nothochrysa fulviceps

3. Plant associations uncertain
  Subilla confinis
  Xanthostigma xanthostigma oak and willow recorded
  Hemerobius marginatus birch, hazel, alder and beech recorded

TABLE 3 (CONTINUED)

SPECIES APPARENTLY CONFINED TO CONIFEROUS TREES BUT NOT CONFINED TO WOODLAND

S. pseudouncinata Cupressaceae in gardens
P. fuscipennis confined to Scots pine?
A. juniperi confined to Juniper?
H. fenestratus confined to Scots pine?
H. simulans Larch, spruce and pine recorded
H. stigma
H. pini
H. nitidulus
W. ravus confined to Scots pine?
S. fuscescens confined to Scots pine?

SPECIES APPARENTLY CONFINED TO BIRCH TREES BUT NOT CONFINED TO WOODLAND

H. perelegans

SPECIES APPARENTLY CONFINED TO OAK TREES BUT NOT CONFINED TO WOODLAND

Both species are also reported as being disturbed from other tree species, but in all cases oaks were also present. Adults may, of course, rest on a wide variety of trees or other objects.

H. micans
S. pygmaeus

SPECIES ASSOCIATED WITH FRESHWATER HABITATS

S. fuliginosa fast and slow rivers, but not torrents?
S. lutaria slow flowing and static water with mud bottom
S. nigripes requirements unknown
O. fulvicephalus watercourses lined with damp mosses
Sisyra fuscata larvae parasitic in sponges – *Spongilla lacustris* and *Ephydatia fluviatilis* recorded
S. dalii
S. terminalis

SPECIES ASSOCIATED WITH WOOD SAGE *TEUCRIUM SCORODONIA* ON ROCKY SLOPES

M. hirtus

SPECIES ASSOCIATED WITH STABLE SAND DUNES WITH MARRAM GRASS *AMMOPHILA ARENARIA*

W. balticus
C. abbreviata

SPECIES ASSOCIATED WITH SANDY SOILS

E. nostras larva excavates a pit into which ants and other prey fall

TABLE 3 (CONTINUED)

SPECIES ASSOCIATED WITH MOSS ON GROUND, LOGS, ETC

Boreus hyemalis

SPECIES RECORDED FROM A WIDE VARIETY OF HABITATS

C. psociformis broad-leaved deciduous trees and bushes; not recorded on pine
C. pineticola possibly associated with a variety of conifers
C. tineiformis broad–leaved deciduous trees
C. borealis unknown. possibly associated with mature oak but also dislodged from sycamore and birch
C. pygmaea deciduous and coniferous associations recorded
S. aleyrodiformis recorded from a variety of deciduous trees and shrubs
H. humulinus larvae on a variety of deciduous trees and shrubs
H. lutescens larvae on a variety of deciduous trees and shrubs
W. nervosus larvae on a variety of deciduous trees and shrubs
W. subnebulosus larvae on a variety of deciduous trees and shrubs
S. elegans deciduous woodland, neutral grassland, gardens, hedges
C. perla possibly a species of grassland with scrub
C. pallens frequently captured in gardens
C. carnea agg. ubiquitous, but especially on oak trees
C. ciliata absent from truly urban areas?
C. albolineata most frequent in woodland and gardens
D. flavifrons ubiquitous, but perhaps associated with conifers
D. prasina most records are from grassland at the edge of woodland but there are also records from more
open areas of heath, downland and sand dunes
D. ventralis possibly associated with pine but there are some records from deciduous woodland too
P. cognata perhaps associated with chalky soils
P. communis usually in association with brambles in edge habitats
P. germanica usually in association with brambles in edge habitats

SPECIES WHERE HABITAT ASSOCIATION IS UNKNOWN

C. esbenpeterseni only recorded from light traps
C. lentiae only recorded from light traps
Helicoconis sp. ? *hirtinervis* in litter under heather on coastal sand dune
P. diptera possibly associated with grass growing in tussocks in a variety of habitats.
M. angulatus low herbage
M. paganus low herbage, but also from trees
M. variegatus low herbage
W. malladai Scottish Highlands only
W. mortoni extinct in Britain
S. pellucidus old literature says confined to pines, but recent records all relate to oaks. Perhaps
mis–identified in the past?
D. phalaenoides most records in woodland, but some from scrub and a few from grassland
C. phyllochroma formerly confused with *C. commata*; no information on associations available
C. commata grassland ?
C. bellifontensis perhaps associated with pines?
N. capitata thought to be associated with pine but recent insecticidal fogging of oak canopy also revealed
this species
N. inpunctata single British specimen from a light trap. Possibly associated with scrub oaks in Europe

How to Use the Keys

These keys have been written to enable any person – even an inexperienced user – to identify British lacewings and their allies. You may enter the keys at whichever point you find the most appropriate. If you are unfamiliar with insects key A will tell you whether or not the specimen is a lacewing and to which major group (snake flies, alder flies, true lacewings or scorpion flies) it belongs; it can be used easily on living insects. If it is already known to which of these four major groups the insect belongs, you may progress to Keys B (species of scorpion fly), C (species of snake fly), D (species of alder fly) or E (families of true lacewings). From Key E you will be directed first to the family to which the insect belongs and then via one further key, or in some cases two, to the species.

Each key follows the traditional dichotomous form: that is, it consists of pairs (couplets) of contrasting descriptions (leads) – one of which matches the characteristics of the insect, the other does not. Starting at couplet 1, choose the description which fits your specimen and follow the instruction given, which will either be the number of the next couplet to which you should proceed or the name and number of the next key to use. Eventually, you will arrive at the name of the species. It is absolutely essential to read both leads of a couplet before making a decision on which couplet to go to next: a wrong choice will lead you to the wrong part of the key and correct identification will then be impossible. Interpret the descriptions literally; where there is ambiguity a series of 'either/or' choices will be given. Very occasionally, there will be three choices rather than two. Where this is the case apply the same procedure and choose whichever of the three contrasting leads fits your specimen.

Although some features will be visible to the unaided eye, a hand lens or low power binocular microscope is likely to prove necessary for correct determination of some species. For most, a magnification of x20 will be adequate, but for looking at some features x40 will be better. For the correct identification of the wax flies a magnification of x20 with good, white lighting will reveal as much detail as x40 with poor yellow lighting. Two lights are generally better than one, as they eliminate shadows if positioned one each side.

Every effort has been made to construct keys that can be used on living insects 'in the field'. However, in some cases, especially where it is essential to examine the internal genital structures in order to arrive at the name of the insect, a dead specimen is unavoidably required. Hints on collecting and preserving specimens where this is required are given in Appendix 2, on page 262.

KEY A

IS IT A LACEWING?

1   Less than six legs, or front pair reduced and non-functional ....*not a lacewing*

—   Six fully functional legs present (take care that none have been broken off your specimen) **2**

2   Either less than four wings, or with the fore wings not membranous and not adapted for flight or with fore wings vestigial (see Fig. 5b), or fore wings modified into stiff spines, or some other combination (see Fig. 5c) **3**

—   Four wings present (hind pair may be much reduced so look carefully). Front pair of wings, and also the hind pair if fully developed, always membranous and fully developed for flight **4**

3   Head with a downwards pointing 'beak' which bears the jaws at the tip (Fig. 5a). Fore wings greatly reduced and insect like Figure 5b, or fore wings modified into stiff spines and insect like Figure 5c ....Scorpion flies MECOPTERA (Key B, page 198)

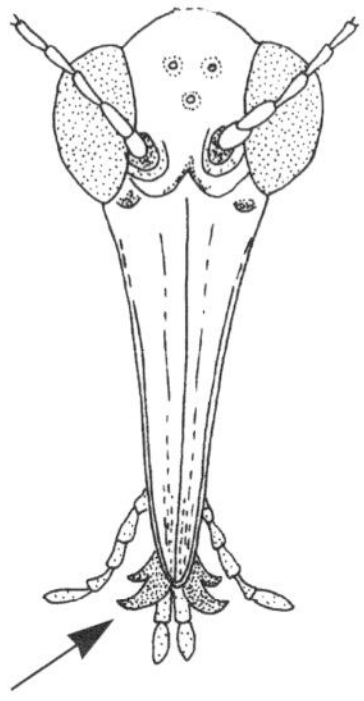

Fig. 5a

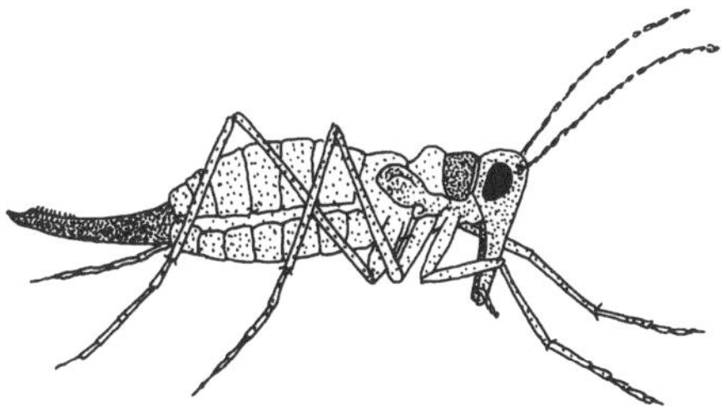

Fig. 5b

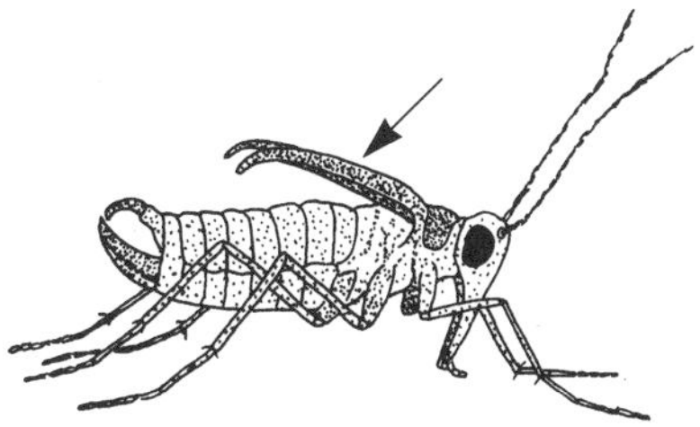

Fig. 5c

—   No such 'beak' and insects not like Figures 5a-c ....*not a lacewing*

4 Head with a downwards pointing 'beak' which bears the jaws at the tip (see Fig. 5a). Males with swollen genital capsule at the tip of the abdomen, which is held forwards over the body like a scorpion in a live insect (Fig. 6a). Female abdomen 'normal' (Fig. 6b). Wing membranes clear, patterned with black or dark brown patches in some species, unmarked in others ....
....Scorpion flies MECOPTERA (Key B, page 198)

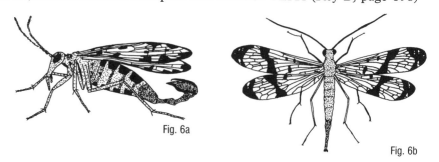

Fig. 6a

Fig. 6b

–   Not like this; no beak and insects not at all like Figures 6a,b **5**

5 Wings never held over body like a tent; held folded back like a butterfly (Fig. 7a) or flat over the body (Fig. 7b) or some other way ....*not a lacewing*

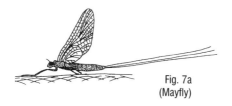

Fig. 7a
(Mayfly)

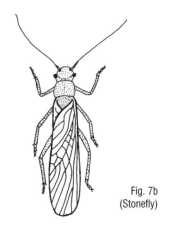

Fig. 7b
(Stonefly)

–   Wings held over the body like a tent in living insects (Fig. 8). In dead specimens, the wings are usually still held over the body in this manner but occasionally some species may die with their wings folded back like a butterfly. If in doubt, continue here **6**

Fig. 8

6 Fore wings with several cross-veins. (If in doubt, continue here) **11**

–   Fore wings with very few, or completely without, cross-veins **7**

7   Wings with hairs arising directly from the membrane as well as from the veins. Usually these insects are very densely hairy but specimens from moth traps or malaise traps may often be so worn that few hairs remain ....
....*not a lacewing (Caddis fly)*

–   Any hairs on the wings arise from the veins; absolutely no hairs arising from the wing membrane on any wing. Small insects, less than 5mm long, usually white or grey, but sometimes very dark, blackish-grey or with transparent wings **8**

8   Fore wings more or less transparent ....*not a lacewing*

–   Fore wings not transparent, often whitish or grey, sometimes darker **9**

9   Abdomen with two tube-like 'spines' on upper surface (Fig. 9) ....*not a lacewing (Aphid)*

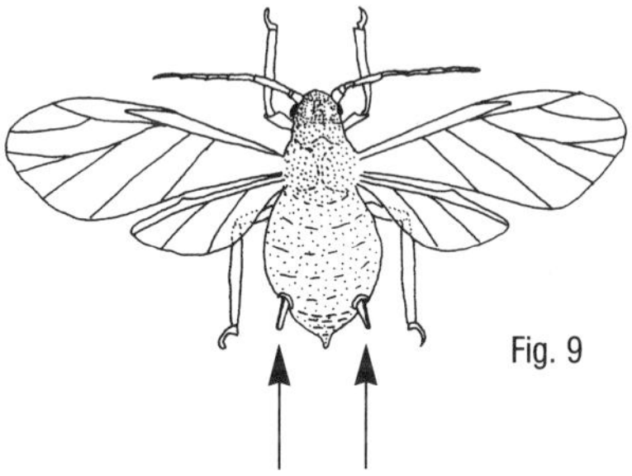

Fig. 9

–   Abdomen without these two 'spines' on upper surface **10**

10   Insects covered in a white or greyish 'waxy' powder on the body and usually on the wings (though this can rub off). Fore wings with venation similar in pattern to Fig. 10, and cross-veins present. Hind wings fully developed or greatly reduced ....Wax flies
CONIOPTERYGIDAE
(Keys E and F, pages 207 and 211)

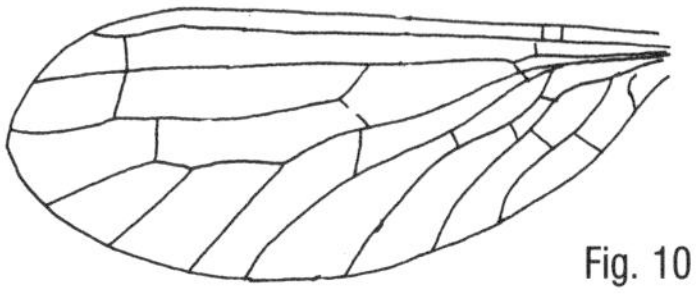

Fig. 10

–   Fore wings with venation greatly reduced (Fig. 11a) or very simple (Figs. 11b,c) or resembling that in Fig. 10, without cross-veins ....*not a lacewing*

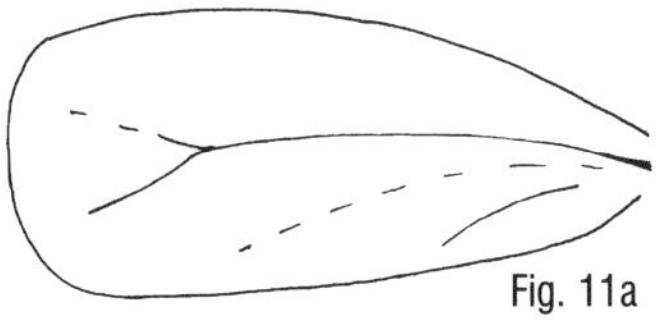

Fig. 11a 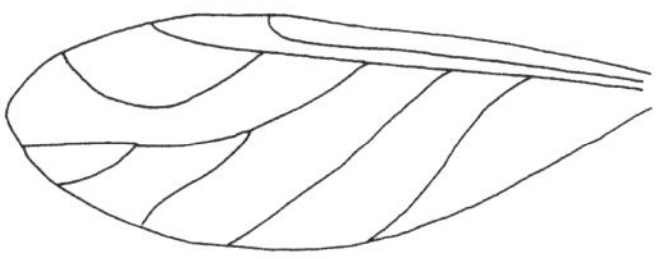   Fig. 11b 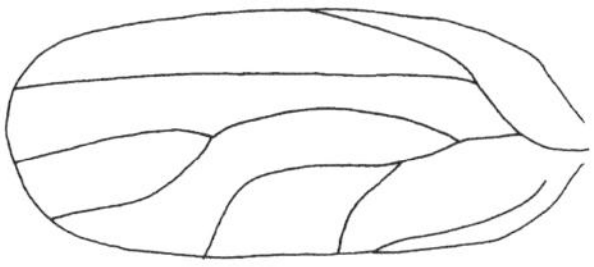   Fig. 11c

11 Small or minute insects, less than 5 millimetres long, covered in a white or greyish 'waxy' powder on the body and usually on the wings (though this can rub off). Fore wings with venation similar in pattern to Fig. 12. Hind wings fully developed or greatly reduced. Wings never with transparent membranes ....Wax flies
CONIOPTERYGIDAE
(Keys E and F, pages 207 and 211)

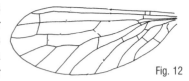

Fig. 12

– Not like this. Larger insects or, if small, then the wing membrane is either clear (with or without a pattern) or brown **12**

12 Pronotum (between the thorax and the head) greatly elongated (Fig. 13a). Female with long 'needle-like' ovipositor (Fig. 13b) ....Snake flies
RAPHIDIOPTERA (Key C, page 203)

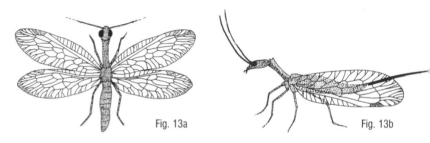

Fig. 13a   Fig. 13b

– Not like this **13**

13 Tip of abdomen with short 'cerci' (Fig. 14a) or longer 'tails' (Fig. 14b) ....
....*not a lacewing*

Fig. 14a   Fig. 14b

– Tip of abdomen without cerci or 'tails' **14**

14 Each antenna shorter than the width of the head ....*not a lacewing*

– Each antenna longer than the width of the head **15**

15 Tarsus not with five segments (usually with three) ....*not a lacewing*

– Tarsus with five segments (Fig. 15) **16**

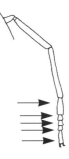

Fig. 15

16 Blackish-brown insects, with wing length greater than 10 mm, resembling Figs. 16a,b. Wings uniformly brownish all over. In the fore wings none, or only a very few, veins fork when they reach the hind margin ....Alder flies
MEGALOPTERA (Key D, page 205)

Fig. 16a

Fig. 16b

– Brownish or green insects (Fig. 17a), and wings usually with transparent or translucent membranes. If the wings are brownish all over then the insect is quite small, with a wing length of less than 10 mm. In the fore wing, most veins fork on reaching the hind margin (eg Figs. 17b,c) ......
...Lacewings NEUROPTERA (Key E, page 207)

Fig. 17a

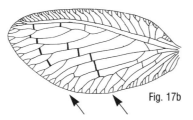

Fig. 17b

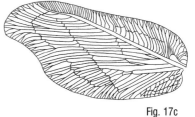

Fig. 17c

KEY B

Species of Scorpion flies (MECOPTERA)

Recognition features: The Mecoptera are the only British insects which possess the downwards pointing conical beak which bears the jaws at the tip (see Fig. 19). The snow-flea is quite distinctive but can be easily missed or overlooked (especially amongst bulk samples from pitfall traps) on account of its small size. Scorpion flies have distinctive wings and the males are readily recognisable by the genital capsule held forwards over the body – the habit which gives the genus its common name. Several additional species are present in Europe and though not yet encountered in Britain, *Panorpa vulgaris* may possibly be present, undetected. Identification of European *Panorpa* species is rather difficult and is not discussed here. However, brightly marked examples of *P. communis* may perhaps include this additional species and voucher specimens should be retained.

1   Insect about 5 mm long. Female with vestigial wings and a distinctive ovipositor (Fig. 18a); male with wings modified into stout spines and lacking an ovipositor (Fig. 18b). Ocelli absent (unlike Fig. 19) ....*Boreus hyemalis* (the snow flea)

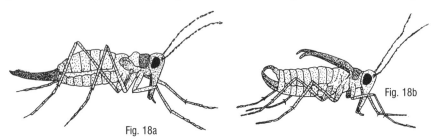

Fig. 18b

Fig. 18a

–   Insect about 10mm long or more and fully winged, with a wingspan of about 20 mm or more. Typically with patterned wings, similar to Figs. 20, 21 but pattern sometimes faint or absent, especially on Scottish specimens. Ocelli present (Fig. 19) **2**

ocelli

Fig. 19

2   Tip of abdomen swollen to form genital capsule
     which is held forwards over the body in the
     manner of a scorpion (Fig. 20) ....
     ....(Key to males) **3**

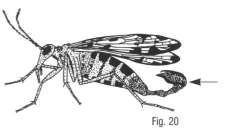

Fig. 20

–   Abdomen tapering to the tip and not held forward
     over the body (Fig. 21) ....(Key to females) **4**

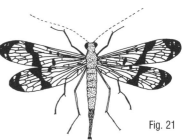

Fig. 21

KEY TO MALES

Look at the lower (ventral) surface of the genital capsule to see the features. Note that if the capsule is held forward over the body then the ventral side will be upwards!

READ THREE CHOICES

3   Lower surface of genital capsule with callipers slender and diverging (Fig. 22) ....
....*Panorpa cognata*

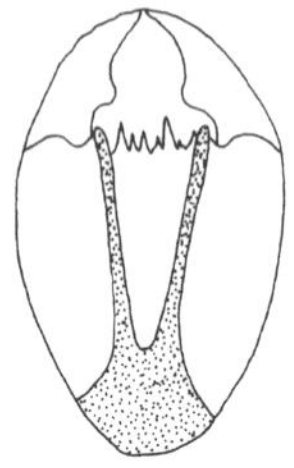

Fig. 22

OR Lower surface of genital capsule with callipers slender, curved outwards at middle and converging at the tips (Fig. 23) ....
....*Panorpa communis*

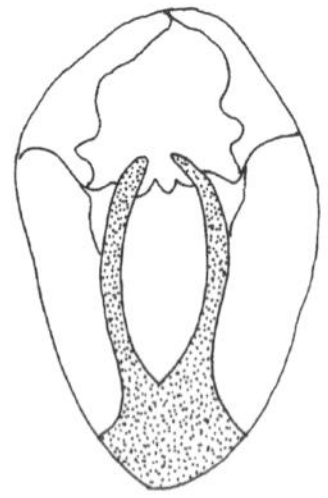

Fig. 23

OR Lower surface of genital capsule with callipers parellel or only slightly diverging and expanded at the tips (Fig. 24) ....*Panorpa germanica*

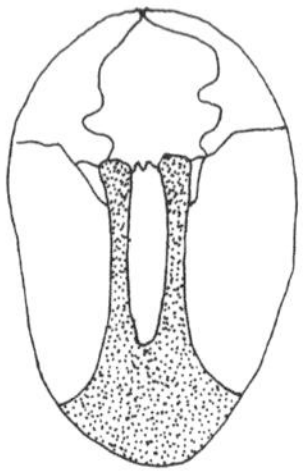

Fig. 24

NOTE: Since the text for these keys went to press, the possible presence in Britain of a fourth species of *Panorpa* – *P. vulgaris* – has been brought to my attention. This species has genital callipers more or less identical to those of *P. communis* and will run to that species in this key. Larger, brighter examples of *P. communis* in which the three basal wing spots are very large and dark may prove to be *P. vulgaris*; it is important that voucher specimens are retained and identification confirmed by examination of the ventral parameres.

KEY TO FEMALES

Females can only be reliably named by examining the shape of the ovipositor. This sits inside the abdomen and needs to be extracted. This is quite an easy process, and is detailed on page 265. Earlier keys using wing characters or abdominal segment shape should be disregarded. Refer to Fig. 25 for the names of the various parts of the ovipositor.

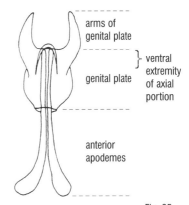

Fig. 25

4   Anterior apodemes (see Fig. 25) absent or vestigial (Fig. 26) ....*P. communis*

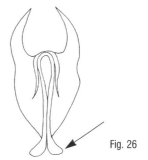

Fig. 26

–   Anterior apodemes (see Fig. 25) well developed (eg. Figs. 27, 28, 29)...............5

5   Anterior apodemes (see Fig. 25) closely parallel for most of their length, though the tips may be splayed (eg. Figs. 27, 28) **6**

–   Anterior apodemes (see Fig. 25) clearly splayed throughout their entire length (eg. Fig. 29) 7

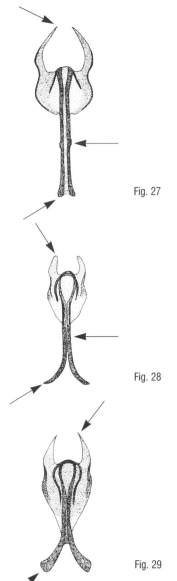

Fig. 27

Fig. 28

Fig. 29

6   Arms of genital plate about as long as the plate, narrow and with acutely pointed tips. Lateral margins of plate sinuate. Anterior apodemes usually with a rough swelling at about mid-point (sometimes absent). Overall impression is of a small square plate with very long, straight apodemes (Fig. 27) ....*P. germanica*

–   Arms of genital plate shorter than the plate and wider with blunt or rounded tips as in Fig. 28. No swelling on anterior apodemes. Overall appearance of a long narrow plate with short, straight apodemes ....*P. cognata*
(teneral or damaged specimen)

7   Anterior apodemes short and flattened, or else very broad, diverging broadly throughout most or all of their length. Tips of arms of genital plate tapering to points (Fig. 29) ....*P. communis*

–   Anterior apodemes longer, and parallel for much of their length before the tips diverge (as in Fig. 28) **8**

8   Tips of arms of genital plate rounded. Tips of anterior apodemes slender, usually rounded or only moderately flattened, and tapering (as in Fig. 28) ....*P. cognata*

–   Tips of arms of genital plate pointed. Anterior apodemes widening at the tips which are usually broadly flattened (as in Fig. 29) ....*P. communis*

KEY C

SPECIES OF SNAKE FLIES (RAPHIDIOPTERA)

Recognition features: The combination of the elongated pronotum (Figs. 30a,b) AND the presence of four, fully developed membranous wings is unique amongst the British insect fauna. The pterostigma on the forewing has at least one cross-vein running through it and three ocelli are present on the top of the head though these can be difficult to see. Female snake flies have a rather 'needle-like' ovipositor arising from the end of the abdomen, similar to that seen on some parasitic Hymenoptera (the name of the group is derived from the Greek Raphidas = a needle, relating to this ovipositor); males lack this long appendage.

The Raphidioptera are a large group, but in Britain we have only four species. Apart from *Raphidia ophiopsis* (see key couplet 2), which may perhaps be present in Scotland, it is considered very unlikely that further species will be found in Britain.

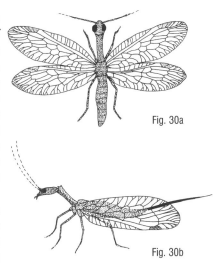

Fig. 30a

Fig. 30b

1   In the fore wing, the basal vein of cell number 1 (see Fig. 31) is basal to the end of the pterostigma so that the pterostigma starts at about a third of the way or half way along cell 1 (see Fig. 32, arrows a and b) **2**

–   In the fore wing, the basal vein of cell number 1 (see Fig. 31) more or less coincides with the basal end of the pterostigma (see Fig. 33, arrows a and b) **3**

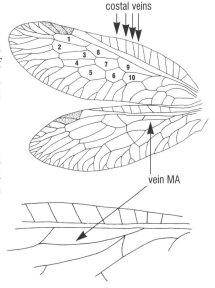

costal veins

vein MA

Fig. 31

2   In the fore wing, the distal vein of cell 1 (see Fig. 31) coincides with the pterostigma, so that the pterostigma extends beyond the tip of cell 1 (Fig. 32, arrow c). Vein R continues beyond pterostigma and reaches the wing tip without forking (Fig. 32, arrow d) ....
............................*Atlantoraphidia maculicollis*

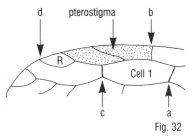

Fig. 32

–   In the fore wing, the distal vein of cell 1 (see Fig. 31) lies beyond the end of the pterostigma (Fig. 33, arrow c). Vein R continues beyond the pterostigma and forks at the tip (Fig. 31 and Fig. 33, arrow d). Pterostigma usually contains at least two cross-veins. Costal space usually with at least 12 costal veins (see Fig. 31, arrows) ....
....*Phaeostigma notata*

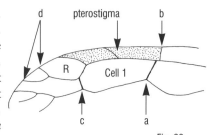

Fig. 33

NOTE: A fifth species, *Raphidia ophiopsis* Linnaeus, occurs widely in Fenno-Scandia and central Europe and may perhaps be found in Scotland. In this key, it will run to *Phaeostigma notata*, but only has a single cross-vein in the pterostigma and has less than ten costal cross-veins. Any specimen which does not fit *Phaeostigma notata* correctly should be sent to an appropriate person for checking.

3   In the hind wing, the basal portion of vein MA (see Fig. 31) is short and straight, resembling a cross-vein (Fig. 34) ...*Xanthostigma xanthostigma*

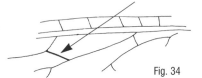

Fig. 34

–   In the hind wing, the basal portion of vein MA (see Fig. 31) is long and sinuous, not at all like a cross-vein (Fig. 35) ....*Subilla confinis*

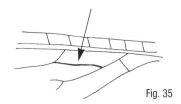

Fig. 35

Key D

SPECIES OF ALDER FLIES (MEGALOPTERA)

Recognition features: Fairly large (wing length over 10 mm), dark brown to blackish insects, with the unpatterned wings more or less uniformly brown all over, though the veins may be darker than the membrane. Wings held over the body in tent-like manner (Fig. 36a). Antenna shorter than the length of one wing. Tip of abdomen lacking appendages (tails, spines etc) (Fig. 36b). Several costal cross-veins present. Only one cross-vein in the subcostal space (between veins Sc and R), about half way along the wing (Fig. 36c). Vein Sc fuses with R. Most veins meeting the wing margin do so without forking at the margin. Ocelli absent. Usually near water. The single European genus, *Sialis*, contains three additional species in Europe, two of which may possibly spread to Britain, although this is considered unlikely.

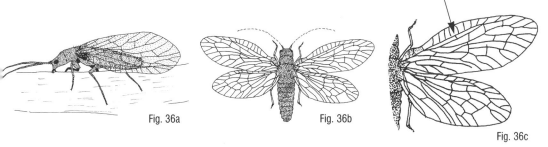

Fig. 36a   Fig. 36b

Fig. 36c

Separation of the three British species relies entirely upon examination of the genitalia (in males) or the anal plates (in females). These features are normally quite easily seen in fresh specimens or if specimens are preserved in alcohol or other fluids. Pinned material, however, will normally require the abdomen to be detached and soaked before examination is possible (see page 265), although if the male genitalia are splayed during setting and held open with a couple of micro pins, the features will be visible in most cases. Wing venation is extremely variable and quite unreliable as a means of identifying species and should not be used at all.

1   Tip of abdomen hinged in the vertical plane so that it opens up to reveal the genital structures (Figs. 38, 39, 40 overleaf) ....(males) **2**

–   Tip of abdomen rounded, without openings. Viewed from below, the tip of the abdomen bears distinctive anal plates (Figs. 37a,b,c) though these may not be visible in dried specimens ....(females) **3**

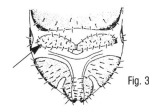
Fig. 37a

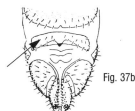
Fig. 37b

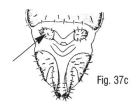
Fig. 37c

READ THREE CHOICES

The arrows in Figs. 38 to 43 indicate the features to look for.

2   Tip of abdomen in side (lateral) view like Fig. 38a
     and in rear (caudal) view like Fig. 38b ....
     ....*Sialis fuliginosa*

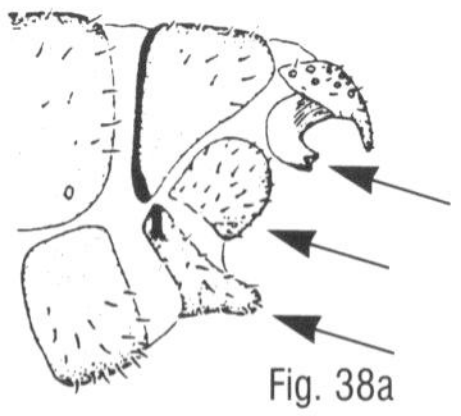

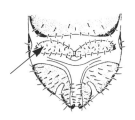

Fig. 38a 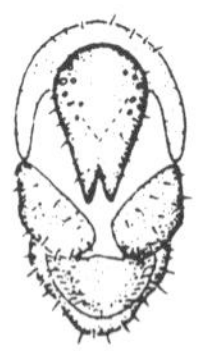   Fig. 38b

OR   Tip of abdomen in side (lateral) view like Fig. 39a
     and in rear (caudal view) like Fig. 39b ....
     ....*Sialis lutaria*

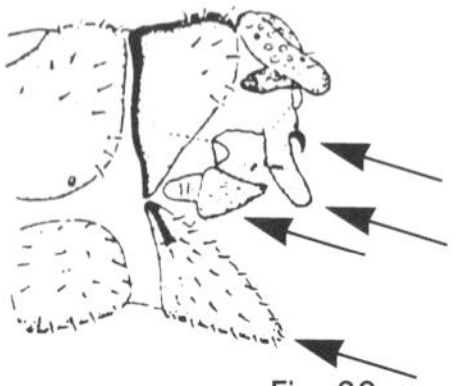

Fig. 39a    Fig. 39b

OR   Tip of abdomen in side (lateral) view likeFig. 40a
     and in rear (caudal) view like Fig. 40b ....
     ....*Sialis nigripes*

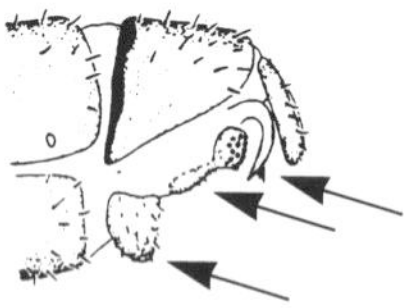

Fig. 40a 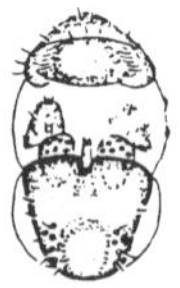   Fig. 40b

NOTE: A caudal view is a tail-on view, the opposite of a head-on view; the insect is aligned with its head pointing directly away from the observer.

READ THREE CHOICES

3   Anal plates as in Fig. 41 ....*Sialis fuliginosa*

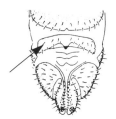

Fig. 41

OR   Anal plates as in Fig. 42 ....*Sialis lutaria*

Fig. 42

OR   Anal plates as in Fig. 43 ....*Sialis nigripes*

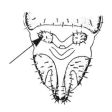

Fig. 43

KEY E

SPECIES OF TRUE LACEWINGS (NEUROPTERA)

Recognition features: Head with large compound eyes widely separated in both sexes. Ocelli absent (except in Osmylidae). Antennae longer than width of head but shorter than length of one wing. Wings membraneous, with or without patterning, held in tent-like manner over the body. Tip of abdomen without cerci or other appendages. Tarsus with 5 segments. The group includes the ant-lions, sponge flies, the green lacewings, the brown lacewings and the giant lacewing. Several other families are present in Europe, though none is at all likely to occur in the British Isles.

1   Small insects with a wingspan usually less than 5mm, usually white though sometimes dark greyish. Body and wings covered in a white (or grey), powdery wax (this can be very hard to see if specimens are preserved in alcohol or other fluids). Longitudinal veins of wings not forked at wing margins. Costal space of fore wings without costal cross-veins (Fig. 44a) except in some species which may have one (Fig. 44b) or two cross-veins (Figs. 44c) near the base of the wing ....
....Coniopterygidae (key F. page 211) Wax flies

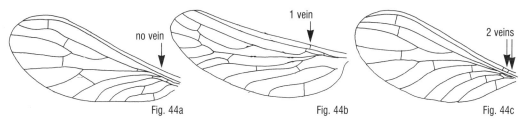

Fig. 44a   Fig. 44b   Fig. 44c

NOTE: Confusion is possible with some aphids, which have different venation (Fig. 45a) and which either have two spines projecting upwards from the abdomen or have two obvious pores in this position, with Psocoptera, which have different venation (Fig. 45b) and transparent wings, with some psyllids which have different venation (Fig. 45c) and with whitefly (Hemiptera: Aleyrodidae) which have greatly reduced venation (Fig. 45d).

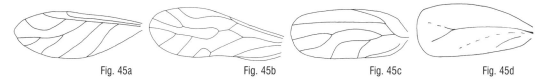

Fig. 45a   Fig. 45b   Fig. 45c   Fig. 45d

–   Insects not like this. Costal space of fore wings with several cross-veins (e.g., Figs. 46, 47, 49). Longitudinal veins usually forked at the wing margins 2

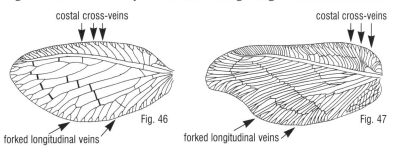

costal cross-veins   costal cross-veins

Fig. 46   Fig. 47

forked longitudinal veins   forked longitudinal veins

2   Large insects, resembling damselflies (Odonata)
     with fore wing length over 25 mm and with the
     antennae longer than width of head and thickened
     at the tip (Fig. 48). Wings with dark spots ....
     ....Myrmeleontidae (ant lions) (page 259)

Fig. 48

NOTE: A single British species, *Euroleon nostras*, so far only recorded from the Suffolk
sandlings and the Channel Islands, but perhaps overlooked elsewhere.

–   Fore wing length less than 25 mm. Antennae
     filamentous, never thickened at the tip 3

3   Wing membrane distinctly patterned with dark
     spots on a clear background (Fig. 49). Three ocelli
     present on the front of the head above the
     antennae. Fore wing length approximately 20 mm.
     A distinctive species ....Osmylidae
                          (the giant lacewing) (page 260)

Fig. 49

NOTE: A single British species, *Osmylus fulvicephalus*.

–   Ocelli absent from the top of the head. Fore wing
     16mm or less OR if longer the wings are not
     marked with dark spots like those in Fig. 49 4

4 Green, brownish-green or yellow-green insects, sometimes marked with black or a pink tinge, and with the fore wing resembling Fig. 50a OR large, brownish insects with a wing length of 15 mm or greater and the fore wing resembling Fig. 50b. Hind margin of fore wing with a vein (Fig. 50c – not like Fig. 51b). Microtrichia (see note 1 below) absent from the wing membrane (use a magnification of x40 or greater). Fore wing never with a recurrent humeral vein (see note 2 below – NOT like Fig. 51a) ....Chrysopidae (Key H, page 221)

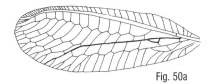 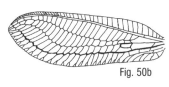 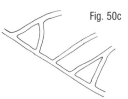

Fig. 50c

Fig. 50a   Fig. 50b

– Insects never green. Usually brown or brownish, sometimes with yellowish reflections at certain angles of light. Recurrent humeral vein (Fig. 51a) may be present or absent. (see note 2 below). Fore wing without a vein running along the hind margin; instead, the membrane of the wing at this edge has small patches of dark-coloured chitin (called trichosors) between the veins – often with a small hair arising from each one (Fig. 51b). Wing membrane with microtrichia, usually visible at x40 or greater magnification (see note 1 below) 5

Fig. 51a

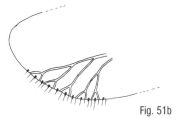

Fig. 51b

NOTE 1: Microtrichia are very short 'hairs' on the membrane of the wing. They appear as small dots over the wing surface and when patches without microtrichia are also present the contrast is easier to see. They are most easily seen by viewing at an angle, rather than by looking straight down on the insect from above.

NOTE 2: Recurrent humeral vein. The humeral vein is the first (basal) cross-vein between the leading edge of the wing (the costa) and the first longitudinal vein (the subcosta). In some species, this cross-vein curves strongly backwards towards the wing base and has several additional cross-veins arising from itself and running to the leading edge of the wing, as shown in Fig. 51a. This is the 'recurrent humeral vein'. In some other species, the humeral vein is angled slightly towards the wing base like Fig. 123 on page 233, but, unless it runs back towards the thorax of the insect and has the additional cross-veins arising from it, then it is not a 'recurrent' humeral vein.

5   Recurrent humeral vein present at the basal end of the costal space in the fore wing (Fig. 52) ....
..................Hemerobiidae (Key I, page 232)

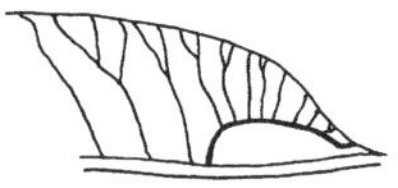

Fig. 52

–   Recurrent humeral vein absent from fore wing (Figs. 53a,b) **6**

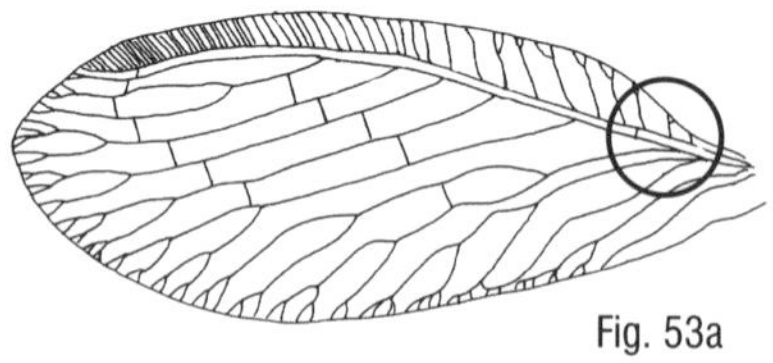

Fig. 53a

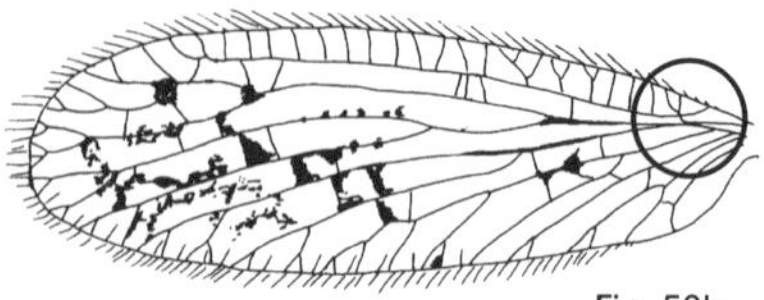

Fig. 53b

6   Hind wings vestigial, usually minute and much smaller than forewings. Fore wing venation and shape as in Fig. 54 ....
.........Hemerobiidae (*Psectra*) (Key I, page 232)

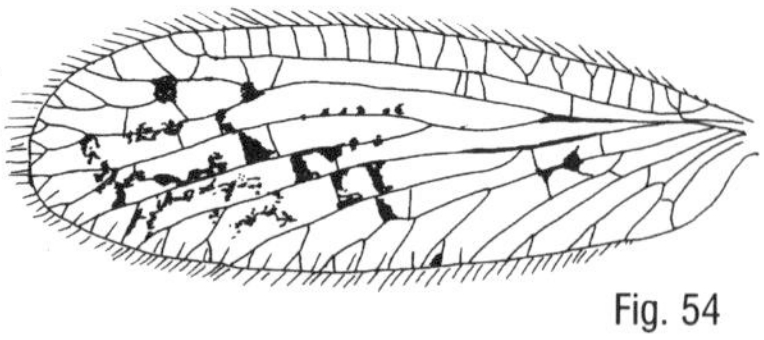

Fig. 54

–   Hind wings fully developed, about the same size as forewings or only slightly smaller 7

7   Most costal cross-veins in the fore wing are unforked (Fig. 55) (usually none are forked, but in some cases a few may be – check both wings to be sure). Fore wings either uniformly brownish (membranes and veins the same colour) or the veins stand out as darker than the membrane. In either case, the membrane never has dark markings except in one species where there may be a single vague dark mark where the anal vein reaches the hind margin ....
...........................Sisyridae (Key G, page 219)

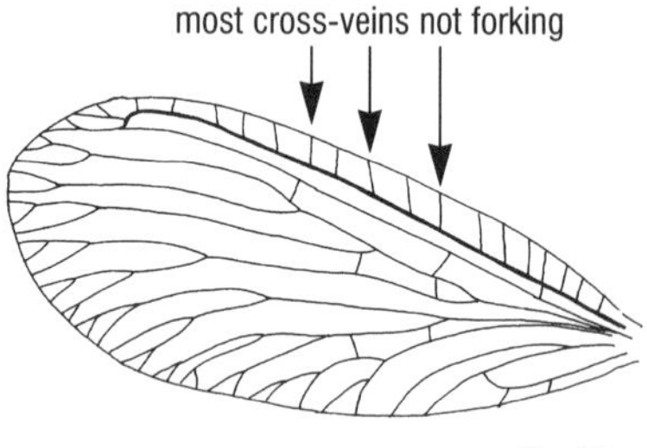

most cross-veins not forking

Fig. 55

–   Many of the costal cross-veins in the fore wing fork before reaching the front margin of the wing (Fig. 56). Fore wing usually with obvious dark markings on the membrane (usually obvious in three of the four species which key out here, but in the fourth species the membrane may appear un-marked) ...
...............Hemerobiidae (*Psectra* and *Micromus*)
(Key I, page 232)

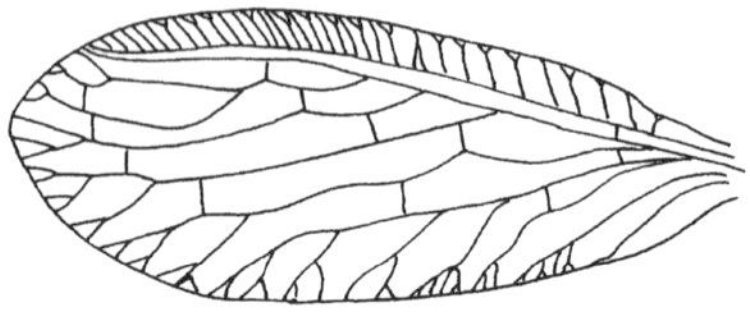

Fig. 56

KEY F

GENERA AND SPECIES OF WAX FLIES (CONIOPTERYGIDAE)

Recognition features: Small, white or grey insects, with wings held over the body like a tent. Body covered in white, waxy powder, including on the wings. Abdomen may be orange in colour, especially in females killed with tetra-chloro-ethane. Can be confused with aphids (which usually have two tube-like spikes projecting upwards from the abdomen – Fig. 9), with Psocoptera (which have transparent wings and different venation – Fig. 45b), with some Psyllids (which have distinctive venation as in Fig. 45c) or with whitefly, Hemiptera: Aleyrodidae (which have a greatly reduced venation – Fig. 45d).

There are eleven species currently known from Britain, plus an additional genus which is represented by an unidentified female. A further 25 species occur in Europe and it is likely that additional species may be discovered in Britain. With the possible exception of *Parasemidalis* which is represented in Europe by just one species, **identifications of species in the remaining genera should always be confirmed by examination of the internal genital structure of the male**. It should be noted that it is not possible to identify females to species level on the basis of current knowledge. Any specimen which can not be identified using this key should be checked against the genitalia drawings in Aspöck, *et al.* (1980).

For convenience, the names of all the veins referred to in the keys are repeated in Fig. 57.

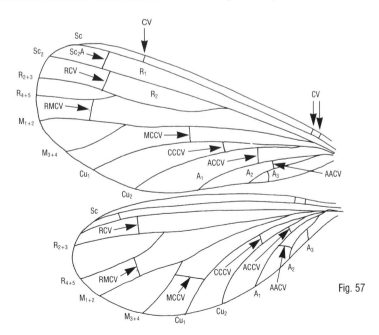

Fig. 57

1   Hind wings vestigial, or at least much reduced (eg. Fig. 58) **2**

Fig. 58

–   Hind wings normal, about the same size and shape as the fore wings (eg. Fig. 59) **4**

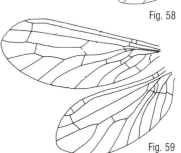

Fig. 59

2   Wings as in Fig. 60. Hind wing short, sub-triangular with rounded corners. In the forewing there is only one costal cross-vein, situated in the basal third of the wing; no cross-vein between veins A1 and A2 (i.e. vein AACV is absent); vein ACCV is obviously basal to the vein CCCV ......
    ....*Helicoconis hirtinervis*

NOTE: See comments after couplet 12. Confirm identification by reference to male genitalia (see page 218)

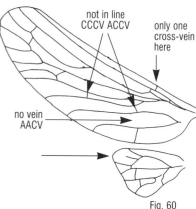

Fig. 60

–   Wings as in Fig. 61. Hind wing long, sub-rectangular or strap-like. In the fore wings, there are two costal cross-veins, situated in the basal third of the wing; vein AACV is present; vein ACCVis more or less in line with vein CCCV ......
    ....*Conwentzia* **3**

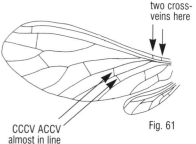

Fig. 61

3   Male abdomen, viewed end-on from rear (caudal view), with the parameres diverging widely (Fig. 62, arrow a) and the processes of the ectoprocts very obviously forked with the upper arm quite long (Fig. 62, arrow b) ......*Conwentzia pineticola*

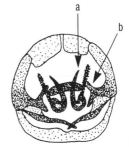

Fig. 62

–   Male abdomen, viewed end-on from rear (caudal view), with the parameres either parallel or diverging only slightly (Fig. 63, arrow a) and the processes of the ectoprocts only a little concave at the tip (Fig. 63, arrow b), nowhere near as clearly bifurcate as in Fig. 62 and the upper arm not produced ....*Conwentzia psociformis*

Fig. 63

NOTE: If the abdomen of male *C. psociformis* specimens preserved in fluid is squeezed (eg. by forceps) the paramers can be splayed unintentionally. If the specimen has splayed parameres, but the processes of the ectoprocts are like Fig. 63b, then the specimen is *psociformis* not *pineticola*. There are currently no other species of *Conwentzia* recorded in Europe.

4   Two cross-veins present between veins R and M in the fore wing (vein RMCV features twice) (Fig. 64) **5**

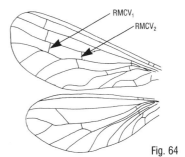

Fig. 64

–   Only one vein RMCV in the fore wing (Fig. 65) **6**

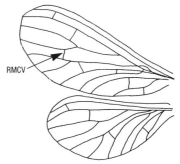

Fig. 65

5 Vein Cu$_2$ in the fore wing sinuous (Fig. 66a) Male genitalia in lateral view like Fig. 66b ....*Aleuropteryx juniperi*

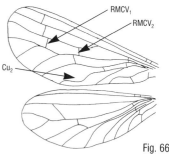

Fig. 66a

Fig. 66b
(after Aspöck *et al.*, 1980)

NOTE: Confirm identification by reference to male genitalia (see page 265). *Aleuropteryx loewii* occurs widely in Europe and could perhaps be found in Britain.

– Vein Cu$_2$ in the fore wing straight (Fig. 67) ....*Helicoconis* **12**

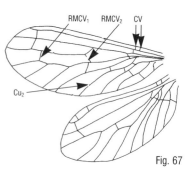

Fig. 67

6 Median vein (M) in hind wing is forked (eg. Fig. 68) – M1+2 and M3+4 are separate **7**

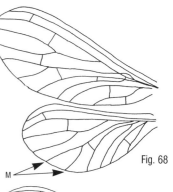

Fig. 68

– Median vein (M) in the hind wing not forked (eg. Fig. 69) – veins M1+2 and M3+4 combine to form a single vein ....*Coniopteryx* **9**

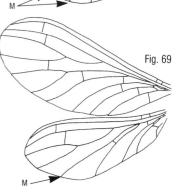

Fig. 69

7   Vein MCCV in the fore wing placed basal to the fork of the median vein M (Fig. 70a). Whole insect is usually dark grey in colour, though sometimes whiter. Male genitalia in lateral view as Fig. 70b ... .*Parasemidalis fuscipennis*

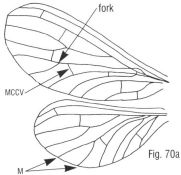

Fig. 70a

NOTE: There are currently no other *Parasemidalis* species known from Europe.

Fig. 70b

–   Vein MCCV in the fore wing placed after the fork of the median vein M as in Fig. 71 or absent altogether ....*Semidalis* 8

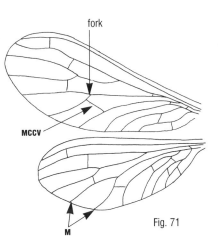

Fig. 71

8   Male genitalia: Lateral view of cleared abdomen (see page 265) as in Fig. 72a; lateral view of parameres as in Fig. 72b ....
..................................*Semidalis aleyrodiformis*

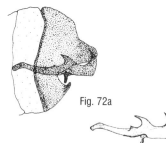

Fig. 72a

Fig. 72b

–   Male genitalia: Lateral view of cleared abdomen as in Fig. 73a; lateral view of parameres as in Fig. 73b ....*Semidalis pseudouncinata*

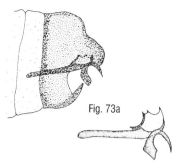

Fig. 73a

NOTE: A third species, *S. vicina* is known from southern Europe and could conceivably spread to Britain in much the same way as did *S. pseudouncinata*.

Fig. 73b

9   Internal genital structures of the male arranged in a ring (Figs. 74a,b) ....
.....................subgenus *Metaconiopteryx* **10**

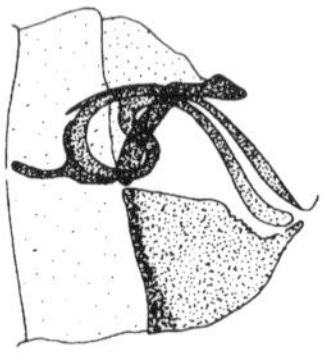

Fig. 74a 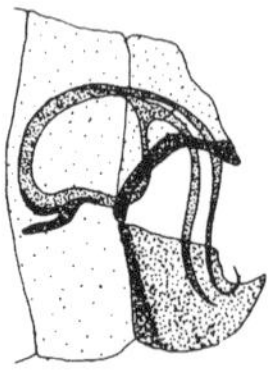   Fig. 74b

–   Internal genital structures of the male not arranged in a ring (eg. Figs. 75a,b) ....
...........................subgenus *Coniopteryx* **11**

Fig. 75a 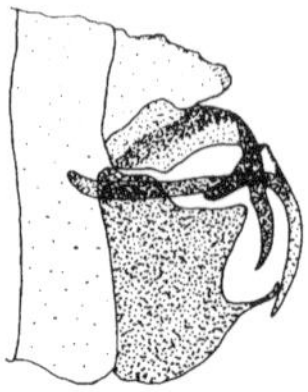   Fig. 75b

10   Fig. 76. Vertical diameter of genital ring quite
      clearly less than the vertical height of the
      hypandrium – usually about half that height or
      less. With the insect aligned with head to the left,
      the parameres are attached to the genital ring
      between the seven and nine o'clock positions ...
      ....*C. (M.) esbenpeterseni*

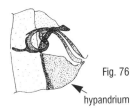

Fig. 76

hypandrium

–   Fig. 77. Vertical diameter of the genital ring
      approximately the same as the vertical height of
      the hypandrium – at any rate clearly greater than
      half of this height. With the insect aligned with its
      head to the left, the parameres attach to the
      genital ring at the six o'clock position ....
      ....*C. (M.) lentiae*

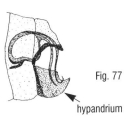

Fig. 77

hypandrium

READ THREE CHOICES

11   Lateral view of cleared abdomen like Fig. 78a.
      Paramere shaped like Fig. 78b ...*C. (C.) borealis*

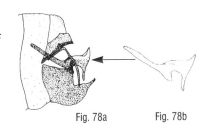

Fig. 78a   Fig. 78b

OR   Lateral view of cleared abdomen like Fig. 79a
      Paramere shaped like Fig. 79b ...*C. (C.) pygmaea*

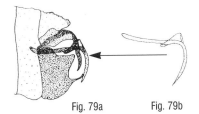

Fig. 79a   Fig. 79b

OR   Lateral view of cleared abdomen like Fig. 80a
      Paramere shaped like Fig. 80b ....
      ....*C. (C.) tineiformis*

NOTE: A number of additional species in the genus *Coniopteryx* occur in Europe and the
possibility of additional species existing undetected in Britain should not be overlooked.

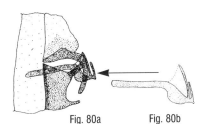

Fig. 80a   Fig. 80b

READ THREE CHOICES

12   Male genitalia in ventral view like Fig. 81 ....
     ....*H. hirtinervis*

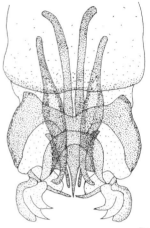

Fig. 81
(after Aspöck *et al.*,
1980)

OR Male genitalia in ventral view like Fig. 82
     ....*H. lutea*

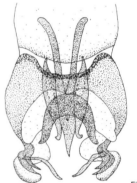

Fig. 82
(after Aspöck *et al.*,
1980)

OR Male genitalia in ventral view different in some
     respect ......*refer to European keys for identification*

Note: The genus *Helicoconis* is recorded in Britain as a single, unidentified female, probably *hirtinervis*, from Scotland, though there is a single old record of *H. lutea* from County Durham which can not be substantiated. Any examples of *Helicoconis* found in Britain should be retained and sent for verification.

KEY G

SPECIES OF SPONGE FLIES (SISYRIDAE)

Recognition features: Small, unicolorous brown lacewings with **no recurrent humeral vein** and none or very few of the costal cross-veins forking. Subcostal space closed as a result of the subcostal vein curving back to fuse with the radial vein before the tip of the wing (Fig. 83a). The sexes may be recognised by the shape of the tip of the abdomen in lateral view – resembling Fig. 83b in males and Fig. 83c in females. A single genus, *Sisyra* containing three British species, one common and widespread, the other two local. There are two additional species in Europe one of which, *S. jutlandica*, could possibly be discovered in Britain. This latter species has the antennae yellow in the basal half and dark at the tip.

Confusion is possible with the genus *Sympherobius* (family Hemerobiidae) which has the recurrent humeral vein present and many costal cross-veins forking before meeting the costa (see Figs. 134, 135 – page 237).

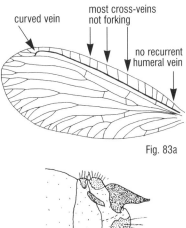

Fig. 83a

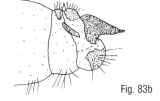

Fig. 83b

Fig. 83c

1   Both sexes with ends of antennae distinctly pale.
     Tip of male abdomen from above as Fig. 84 ......
     ....*Sisyra terminalis*

Fig. 84

—   Both sexes with antennae dark for their entire
     length **2**

2   Both sexes with fore wing uniformly coloured
     brown, the cross-veins scarcely darker than the
     membrane. Tip of male abdomen from above as
     Fig. 85 ....*Sisyra fuscata*

Fig. 85

—   Both sexes with fore wing not uniformly brown,
     the membrane lighter than many of the veins and
     with small but distinct darker marks – at least
     around the cross-veins. Tip of male abdomen from
     above as Fig. 86 ....*Sisyra dalii*

Fig. 86

KEY H

SPECIES OF (MAINLY) GREEN LACEWINGS (CHRYSOPIDAE)

Recognition features: These include the familiar 'green lacewings'. Green, blue-green or yellow-green insects, sometimes marked with black, OR large brown insects with orange heads. Venation is distinctive (eg. Figs. 87, 88). Wings always held tent-like over body at rest – never folded up like a butterfly nor held flat. Cross-veins in costal space un-forked (occasionally one or two veins may be forked but this is unusual). Wing margin without trichosors (see Fig. 51b, page 209).

1   Brown or brownish species, usually with an orange or orange-brown top to the head. Fore wing as in Fig. 87 – veins Psc and Psm run parallel to the hind wing margin and end near the tip of the wing. Thus the main area of the fore wing has three longitudinal veins, all running more or less parallel with each other, and each enclosing a single row of cells. Cell IMC is more or less rectangular **2**

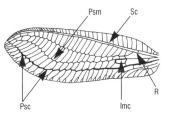

Fig. 87

–   Green, yellow-green, or brownish green species (discolouring yellow or brownish on death). The top of the head green or yellow, sometimes with a black spot or sometimes more extensively black, but never orange or orange-brown. Fore wing as in Fig. 88 – veins Psc and Psm reach the edge of the wing on the rear margin. Thus, the rows of cells in the distal area of the wing are more confused. Cell IMC is triangular, the apex of the triangle pointing towards the wing tip **3**

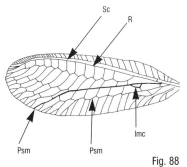

Fig. 88

2   Thorax and pronotum with a broad, pale longitudinal stripe. Head usually bright orange. Tarsal claw toothed at base (Fig. 89). Wing span usually in excess of 40 mm ....
....*Nothochrysa fulviceps*

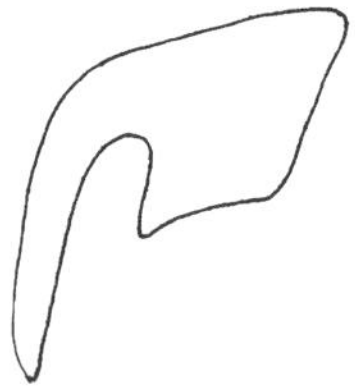

Fig. 89

NOTE: An extremely rare species with only one record since 1958, though perhaps just difficult to find! All records of this species will require confirmation.

—   Thorax and pronotum without a pale stripe, entirely reddish-brown. Head orange-brown. Tarsal claws simple, without swelling at the base (Fig. 90). Wing span typically between 20 and 35 mm ....*Nothochrysa capitata*

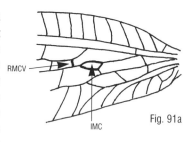

Fig. 90

3   CHECK BOTH WINGS. Apex of cell IMC in forewing not extending as far as, or coinciding with, the vein RMCV (Fig. 91a,b). Wing veins may appear 'hairy' in fresh specimens (view whole insect under low magnification). Green, pink, or pale species often with a brownish mark on the sides of the face and with all wing veins pale (though usually with black hairs). The only species that hibernates as an adult in Britain and so may be found all year ...*Chrysoperla carnea* agg **22**

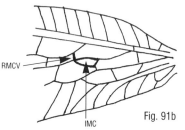

Fig. 91a

Fig. 91b

—   Apex of cell IMC beyond cross vein RMCV (Fig. 92). **If in any doubt, or if the cell IMC and cross-vein are not apparent, key from here** **4**

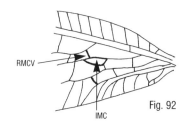

Fig. 92

4   Vein Sc (Fig. 93) black. Top of head similar to Fig. 94 ....*Chrysopa dorsalis*

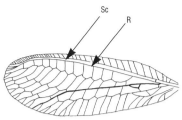

Fig. 93

–   Vein Sc green (or only vaguely darkened). Top of head various (including similar to Fig. 94) 5

NOTE: Rarely, in specimens that have been stored in alcohol in the light, the sub-costal vein of *C. dorsalis* can lose some or all of its black colour. The key works both ways for this species from this couplet so if there is any doubt at all continue to couplet 5.

Fig. 94

5   Second antennal segment (Fig. 95) partly or entirely dark or black 6

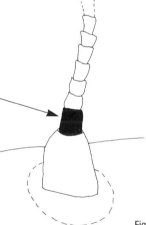

–   Second antennal segment green 12

Fig. 95

6 Extensive black markings between the antennae which connect with black markings that extend over the top of the head (Figs. 96a,b). A blue-green insect with extensive black markings, black ventral surface to the abdomen and many cross-veins black **7**

Fig. 96a   Fig. 96b

–   A discrete black or dark spot present on the head between the antennae separated from any black or dark markings on the top of the head. Top of head either with discrete spots (Figs. 105b,c) or a thin lunule or both (Fig. 105a) or completely unmarked. A green insect, though sometimes with thin dark lines on the side of the thorax or elsewhere **8**

Fig. 105a   Fig. 105b   Fig. 105c

NOTE: For the second part of this couplet, the actual number and arrangement of the dark markings on the top of the head is of no importance

7 Vein Sc (see Fig. 93) green. Dark markings on top of head enclose a smallish more or less circular area of pale colour (Fig. 98a). Tarsal claws toothed at the base (Fig. 98b) ....*Chrysopa perla*

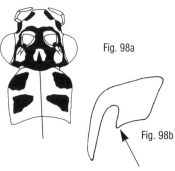

Fig. 98a

Fig. 98b

–   Vein Sc (see Fig. 93) black. Dark markings on vertex enclose a more or less oval or rectangular area of pale colour (Fig. 99a). Tarsal claws simple Fig. 99b) ....*Chrysopa dorsalis*

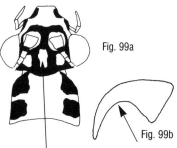

Fig. 99a

Fig. 99b

8   Antennal scape (the large, first segment) with a dark mark on the inner face **9**

–   Antennal scape quite unmarked **10**

(If in doubt, continue here – the key works both ways)

NOTE: Continental specimens of *C. commata* often have a dark mark on the inner face of the antennal scape, but the majority of British specimens lack this. The key works both ways for this species. Voucher specimens should be retained.

9   Sutures (joints between body parts) on side of thorax and on first two or three abdominal segments black, contrasting with the green body (Fig. 100a). Tarsal claws simple (Fig. 100b) ....*Chrysopa commata*

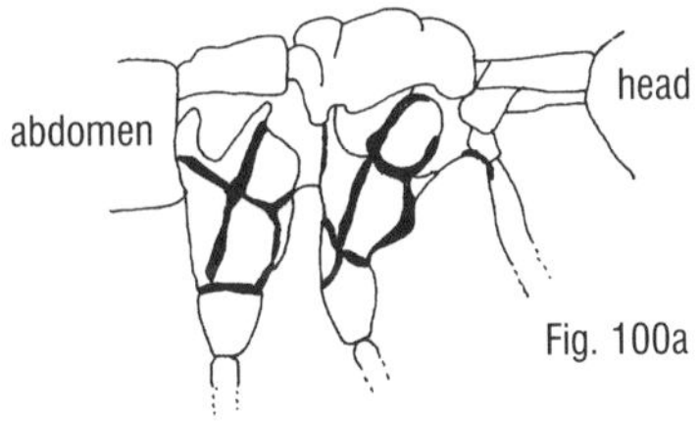

abdomen   head

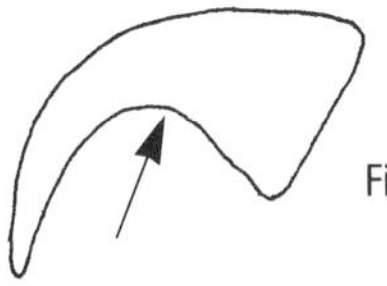

Fig. 100b

Fig. 100a

–   Sides of thorax and abdomen green, without dark lines. Tarsal claws toothed at base (Fig. 101) ......
...................................*Chrysopa   abbreviata*

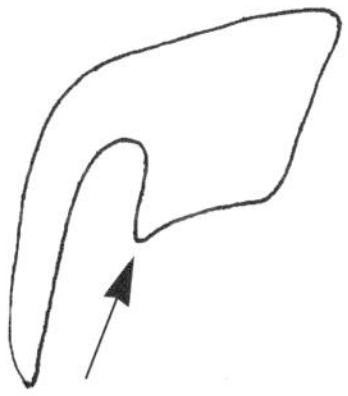

Fig. 101

10   Sutures (joints between body parts) on side of thorax and on first two or three abdominal segments black, contrasting with the green body (see Fig. 100a above). Tarsal claws simple (see Fig. 100b) ....*Chrysopa commata*

–   Sides of thorax and abdomen green. Tarsal claws simple (Fig. 100b) or toothed at the base (Fig. 101) **11**

11   Tarsal claws toothed at the base (see Fig. 101b) ....*Chrysopa abbreviata*

–   Tarsal claws simple (see Fig. 100b) ....*Chrysopa phyllochroma*

NOTE: Look carefully, tilting the specimen at different angles, using good lighting. All six legs have identical claws so try looking at more than one to be certain.

12   A black spot present on head between the bases of the antennae **13**

–   Head green (or pale) between antennae, without a black spot **15**

NOTE: Specimens from light traps can be covered in Lepidoptera wing scales or other debris that may obscure the dark spot between the antennae. It dirt is present, remove it gently with a fine paint brush, either dry or dipped in alcohol or water.

13   Lower (ventral) surface of abdomen glossy black ....*Dichochrysa ventralis*

–   Lower (ventral) surface of abdomen green (but read following note) **14**

NOTE: In fresh specimens, those preserved in alcohol and those that have been cleared in potassium hydroxide the black or green ventral surface of the abdomen is easy to discern. However, in dried specimens the entire abdomen can discolour and give theappearance of being entirely dark in both species. If there is any doubt, it may be necessary to detach the abdomen and either soak it in warm water for a few hours or clear it in potassium hydroxide (see page 265).

14   A dark spot at the base of the costa on each wing (Fig. 102b). Palps ringed with black (usually obvious if specimen is preserved in alcohol but in pinned specimens the palps may appear to be entirely black). Only three or five spots, including the one between the antennae, evident on head (the two spots immediately in front of the antennal insertions are absent) (Fig. 102a). Basal costal cross-vein of fore wing darkened, sometimes quite dark Fig. 102b) ....*Dichochrysa prasina*

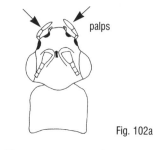

Fig. 102a

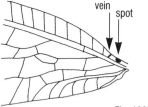

Fig. 102b

NOTE: Occasionally, the two spots below and in front of each eye merge in some specimens to form an elongate 'dash' so giving the impression of three rather than five spots.

–   No dark spot at the base of the costa of any of the wings. Palps green, or sometimes brownish- green, usually darker than head but not black. Head with seven dark spots, including the one between the antennae (Fig 103). Basal costal cross-vein of fore wing pale green, sometimes brownish-green ....*Chrysopa pallens* (= *septempunctata*)

Fig. 103

15 Antennal scape (the largest basal segment) very clearly at least twice as long as wide (Fig. 104a) – usually obvious to the unaided eye. Front edge of fore wing convex (Fig. 104b) – never concave like Fig. 106. Cross-vein SCRCV (see Fig. 104b) is always pale. Fore wing length 16 mm or more (very rarely, diminutive examples may be found with shorter wings ....*Nineta vittata*

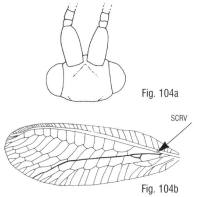

Fig. 104a

Fig. 104b

– Antennal scape not so elongated. It may be more or less square (Fig. 105a) or it may be slightly longer than wide (Fig. 105b) **16**

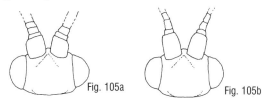

Fig. 105a   Fig. 105b

16 Fore wing length 16 mm or longer. If shorter (rarely, diminutive specimens occur) them EITHER the hairs on the front edge of the fore coxae are dark OR the front edge of the fore wing is concave like Fig. 106 ....**17**

– Fore wing length always less than 16 mm. Front edge of fore wing never concave. Hairs on the front edge of the fore coxae are pale **18**

17 Costal margin of fore wing concave (Fig. 106) with the cilia in the basal fifth (nearest the body) pale and relatively long and thin, at least as long as the width of the costa and sometimes longer than this width. Hairs on the front face of the front coxae pale, long and fine. Costal cross-veins pale ....*Nineta flava*

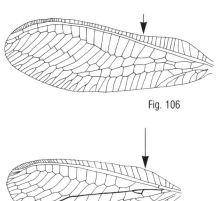

Fig. 106

Fig. 107

– Costal margin of forewing without concavity (Fig. 107), with the cilia in the basal fifth short and stout, scarcely longer than the width of the costa and entirely black. Hairs on the front face of the front coxae short, stout and black. Costal cross-veins entirely dark ......*Nineta inpunctata* (female)

NOTE: *Nineta inpunctata* is known in Britain from a single female specimen taken in North Essex during 1989. It is a seldom captured European species and is un-represented in British collections apart from this single specimen. I have not examined any males, and the key is based on my single female example.

18 All veins of all wings green or pale, never black (though sometimes a few cross-veins may be slightly darkened at one end). Wings veins may appear 'hairy' in fresh specimens (view whole insect under low magnification). Green, pink, or pale species often with a brownish mark on the sides of the face. Apex of cell IMC in forewing not extending as far as cross vein RMCV (Fig. 108a), or else coinciding with this cross vein (Fig. 108b). CHECK BOTH WINGS and refer to Fig. 109b. If this character is present in at least one wing it is this species, but check the other characters as well. The only species that hibernates in Britain and so may be on the wing all year ....
..................*Chrysoperla carnea* group **22**

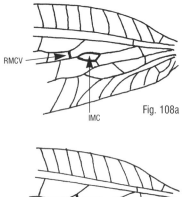

Fig. 108a

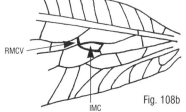

Fig. 108b

– Wings always with some of the cross-veins black, or at least darkened at one end. Green or yellow-green species, never turning pink. Apex of cell IMC ALWAYS extends beyond the cross vein connecting Rs with M, (RMCV) in either wing so that cross vein always contacts the anterior edge of the cell IMC (Figs. 109a and 109b) **19**

NOTE: Finding cell IMC can be difficult for those unfamiliar with the green lacewings. It hangs down below the fourth longitudinal vein of the fore wing as shown diagrammatically in Fig. 109b. Refer also to Fig. 88 to see these veins in the context of the whole wing.

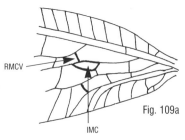

Fig. 109a

Fig. 109b

19 Basal costal cross-vein of fore wing (Fig. 110a) entirely dark. Cross-vein between Sc and R (Fig. 110, arrow b) in fore wing usually pale **20**

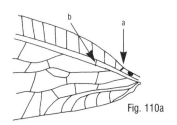

Fig. 110a

– Basal costal cross-vein of fore wing (Fig. 110, arrow a) partly or entirely pale. Cross-vein SCRCV in the fore wing is usually black, or at least darkened (Fig. 110, arrow b) **21**

20 Palps (Fig.111a) dark on inner face (actually ringed with black). A dark spot is usually present at the base of the costa of every wing (Fig.111b). (This can be extremely difficult to see and is sometimes easier to find on the hind wings. If you can find just one spot on one wing, no matter how weak the spot may be, then it counts as being present). Spots on sides of face reddish-brown with margins not always well-defined. Thoracic dorsum never with a pale longitudinal stripe. 'Hairs' on the middle third of the leading edge of the fore wing as in Fig. 111c about 5 or 6 times as long as the width of the costal vein and inclined at an angle of about 45 degrees from the costa, towards the wing tip. The cilia on the costal cross-veins do not quite reach half way across the adjacent costal cells, with some cilia pointing towards the wing tip and some pointing to the base (Fig. 111d) ....
....*Dichochrysa flavifrons*

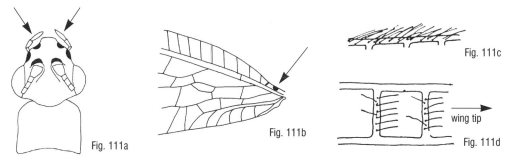

Fig. 111c

Fig. 111a

Fig. 111b

wing tip

Fig. 111d

NOTE: Several other species of *Dichochrysa* occur in Europe and these can be hard to separate. Doubtful specimens should be checked by referring to male genitalia in European texts.

– Palps pale on inner face. Dark spots never present at the base of the costa on any wing. Spots on side of face black and clearly defined. Thoracic dorsum often with a pale longitudinal stripe (can fade in alcohol or be hard to see in dried specimens). 'Hairs' on the middle third of the leading edge of the fore wing as in Fig. 112a, short, only about 2 or 3 times as long as the width of the costal vein and inclined at an acute angle from the costa towards the wing tip. The cilia on the costal cross-veins are about one third as long as the width of the costal cell and usually all point towards the wing tip (Fig. 112b) ......*Cunctochrysa bellifontensis*

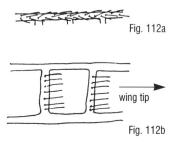

Fig. 112a

wing tip

Fig. 112b

21 Palps usually entirely pale, rarely darkened on outer face only. 'Hairs' on the middle third of the leading edge of the fore wing as in Fig. 113a, about 7 or 8 times as long as the width of the costal vein and more or less perpendicular to the costal vein. 'Hairs' on the costal cross-veins often longer than half the width of the adjacent costal cells and pointing in both directions, thus overlapping with their neighbours (Fig. 113b). Thoracic dorsum never with a pale longitudinal stripe ....*Chrysopidia ciliata*

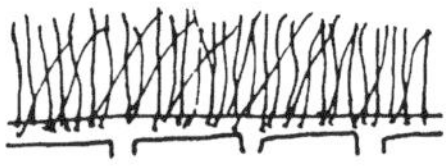

Fig. 113a

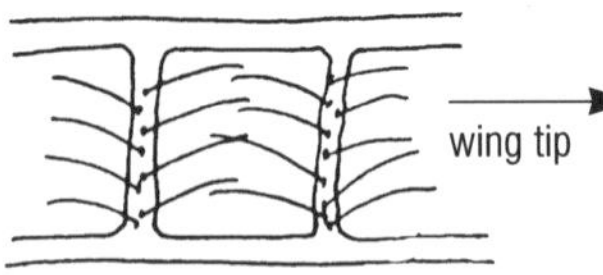

wing tip

Fig. 113b

— Palps always darkened on outer face even if only vaguely so. Cilia on the middle third of the leading edge of the fore wing mostly as in Fig. 114a, about 2 or 3 times as long as the width of the costal vein and usually held tightly adpressed to the costa, all pointing towards the wing tip. Hairs on costal cross-veins rarely more than one third as long as the width of the adjacent costal cells and so never overlapping with their neighbours and usually all pointing towards the wing tip (Fig. 114b). Thoracic dorsum usually with a pale longitudinal stripe, though this can fade in alcohol or be hard to see in dried material ....*Cunctochrysa albolineata*

Fig. 114a

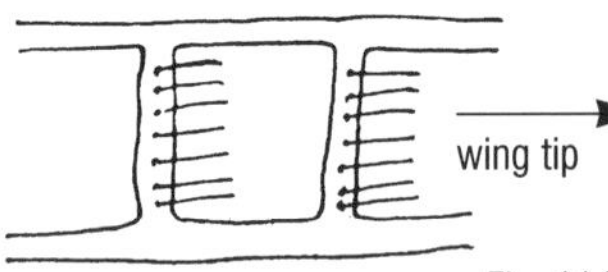

wing tip

Fig. 114b

22 Insect becomes brown during the course of winter hibernation ....*Chrysoperla carnea*

— Insect not becoming brown during winter **23**

NOTE: If trying to key insect outside winter months go to **23**.

23   Membrane between upper and lower surface of the abdomen (Fig. 115) clearly brown at the point nearest the thorax (first two segments). Ignore any brown marks on the tergites or sternites themselves. The tornal region of the fore wing is straightened, which has the effect of making the wing tip appear slightly pointed (see Fig. 116). Insect remains green throughout winter and does not become brown. When comparative material is available, the hairs on the leading edge of the fore wing are shorter than in *C. carnea* ....
......................................*Chrysoperla lucasina*

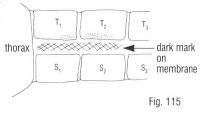

Fig. 115

NOTE: The brown membrane is evidently not always present in examples of this species. When it is, it is usually quite obvious in living insects and in specimens preserved in alcohol or other fluids. It is often visible in dried specimens on pins but where the abdomen has shrivelled and discoloured it may not be possible to see without soaking the specimen.

–   Membrane between upper and lower parts of the abdomen pale, not at all darkened. (If in doubt, continue here). Do not confuse this character with the dark marks which are often present on the tergites **24**

24   The tornal region of the fore wing is straightened, which has the effect of making the wing tip appear slightly pointed (Fig. 116). Insect remains green throughout winter and does not become brown. When comparative material is available, the hairs on the leading edge of the fore wing are shorter than in *C. carnea* ....*Chrysoperla lucasina*

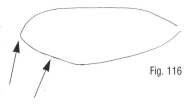

Fig. 116

–   Tornal region of fore wing is evenly curved and so the tip of the wing appears more rounded (Fig. 117). When comparative material is available, the hairs on the leading edge of the fore wing are longer than in *C. lucasina* ....
......................................*Chrysoperla carnea*

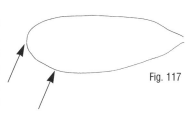

Fig. 117

NOTE: It may not be possible to separate all examples of these two species. In this situation, the insect should be recorded as '*Chrysoperla carnea* group' to avoid erroneous records of the true *carnea* entering the system.

KEY I

GENERA OF BROWN LACEWINGS (HEMEROBIIDAE)

Recognition features: Brown lacewings with a recurrent humeral vein present or, if recurrent humeral vein is absent then either vestigial hind wings, or costal cross-veins forking before meeting the costa or both. One species is unique in having hooked wing tips.

1   Fore wings broad and hooked (falcate) at the tip (Fig. 118). A chestnut-brown coloured species ... .*Drepanepteryx*

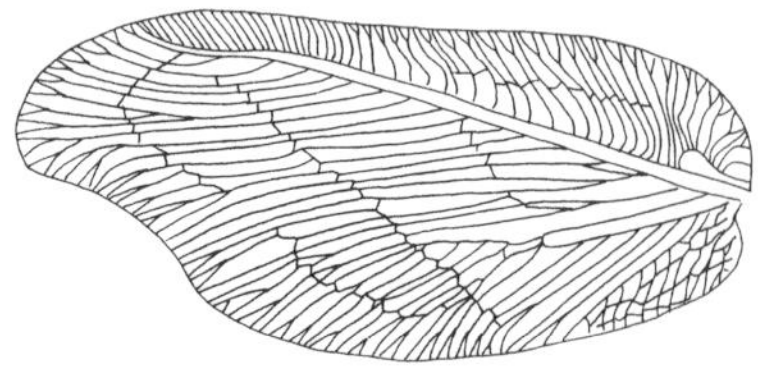

Fig. 118

NOTE: Single British species, *D. phalaenoides* – see page 256.

–   Fore wings rounded at tip (Figs. 119a,b) **2**

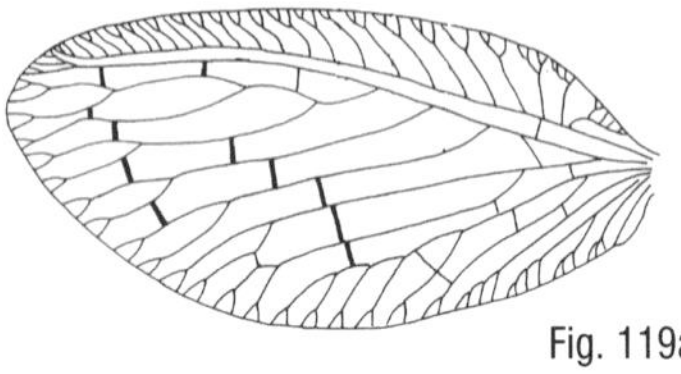

Fig. 119a

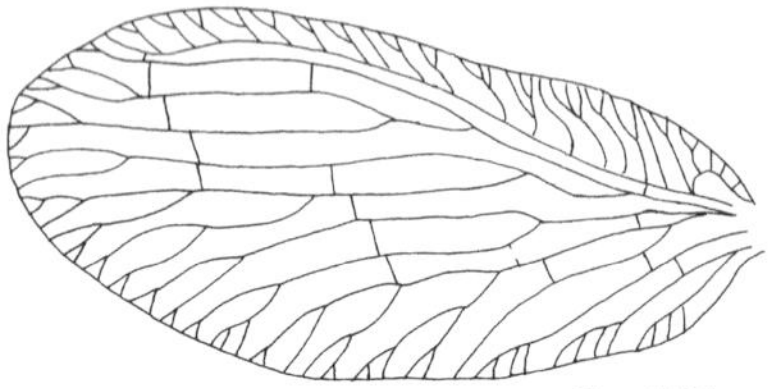

Fig. 119b

2   Hind wings vestigial (**very** much smaller than forewings). Radial sector of fore wing with only two branches (Fig. 120) ....*Psectra*

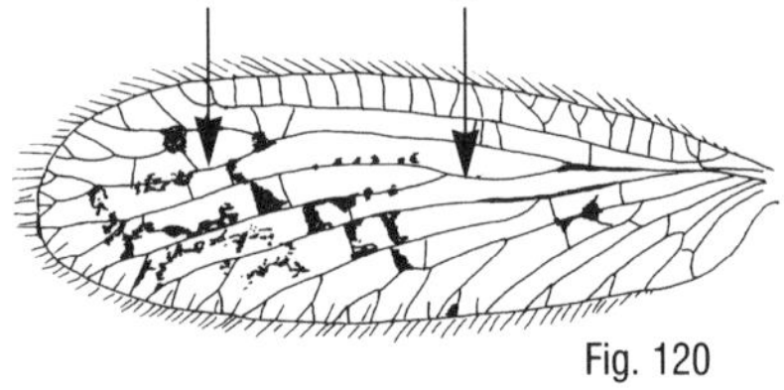

NOTE: A single British species *P. diptera* – see page 257.

Fig. 120

–   Hind wings fully developed (**approximately** the same size as forewings) **3**

3   Recurrent humeral vein absent (e.g. Figs. 121a,b) **4**

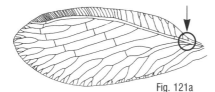
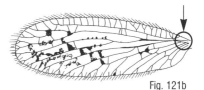

Fig. 121a   Fig. 121b

–   Recurrent humeral vein present (Fig. 122) **5**

Fig. 122

NOTE: Recurrent humeral vein. The humeral vein is the first (basal) cross-vein between the leading edge of the wing – the costa) and the first longitudinal vein (the subcosta). In some species, this cross-vein curves strongly backwards towards the wing base and has several additional cross-veins arising from itself and running to the leading edge of the wing, as shown in Fig. 123. This is the 'recurrent humeral vein'. In some other species, the humeral vein is angled slightly towards the wing base and is forked, as in Fig. 138, but unless it turns sharply beak towards the wing base and has the additional cross-veins arising from it, it is not a 'recurrent' humeral vein.

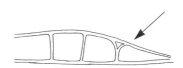

Fig. 123

4   Only two branches to radial vein of fore wing (Fig. 124) ....*Psectra*

NOTE: A single British species *P. diptera* – see page 257.

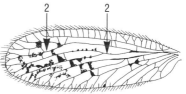

Fig. 124

–   Three (Fig. 125a), four (Fig. 125b) or five Fig. 125c) branches to the radial vein of the fore wing ....*Micromus* (Key J, page 235)

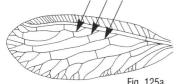
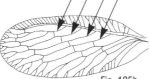
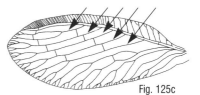

Fig. 125a   Fig. 125b   Fig. 125c

5   Outer third of **hind** wing lacking cross-veins OR if cross-veins present in outer third, then hind wing with no more than four cross-veins altogether ....
....*Sympherobius* (Key K, page 237)

–   Outer third of **hind** wing always with cross veins present AND at least five (often more) cross-veins altogether in hind wing **6**

6   Fore wing with at least five branches to the radial
         vein, sometimes more, and the costal space (the
         space between the leading edge of the wing and
         the first longitudinal vein), broad (Fig. 126) ......
         ....*Megalomus*

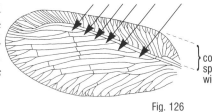

Fig. 126

NOTE: A single British species, *Megalomus hirtus* – see page 257.

–   Fore wing with either three (Fig. 127a) or four (Fig. 127b) branches to the radial
         vein 7

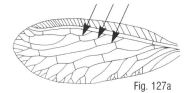

Fig. 127a

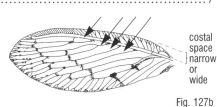

Fig. 127b

7   In the fore wing, vein RMCV in Fig. 128a (see
         note 1, below) either meets vein M before vein M
         forks or else it meets vein M at the point where
         vein M forks (rarely, it may be unpigmented and
         appear absent under low magnification and/or
         poor lighting). In side view, the tip of the abdomen
         of a male specimen resembles Fig. 154a or Fig.
         155a,b. The tip of the female abdomen viewed
         from below lacks anal plates (Fig. 128b) ....
         ....*Hemerobius* (Key L, page 239)

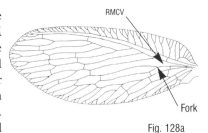

Fig. 128a

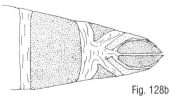

Fig. 128b

–   In the fore wing, vein RMCV is always pigmented
         and evident and meets vein M after vein M has
         forked (Fig. 129). In side view the tip of the
         abdomen of a male specimen resembles Fig.
         157b,c, 162–165. The tip of the female abdomen
         viewed from below has anal plates (but see note 2,
         below) like those in Figs. 158b, 159b, 166-169
         ....*Wesmaelius* (Key M, page 246)

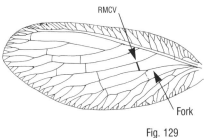

Fig. 129

NOTE 1: The radio-medial cross-vein (RMCV) can be extremely difficult to see, particularly in certain species of *Hemerobius* when it may be quite colourless, and in teneral examples of all species. The shape of the tip of the abdomen of male *Hemerobius* species, however, is usually clear even in dried specimens on pins.

NOTE 2: The female anal plates of *Wesmaelius* can rarely be seen in dried specimens and it is often necessary to soak the abdomen in hot potassium hydroxide in order to clear the abdomen and render them visible (see page 265).

KEY J

SPECIES OF *MICROMUS*

Recognition features: Brown lacewings with no recurrent humeral vein (unlike Fig. 122). There are three British species, two being widespread and common, the other being widespread but local. There are a further two species in Europe, of which one, *M. lanosus* may perhaps occur in southern Britain. This species resembles *M. paganus* but has darker fore wing markings and lacks cross-veins in the hind wing.

1   Only three branches to the radial vein (Fig. 130a). Fore wing membrane clear and transparent, marked with black or very dark brown in a characteristic pattern and hind wing with three characteristic dark marks – one at the apex, and one either side of the apex, the one at the front often coalescing with the apical mark (this species can be recognised on sight without using a key). Wing span (across both wings) less than 15 mm. Tip of male abdomen like Fig. 130b in side view ....*Micromus variegatus*

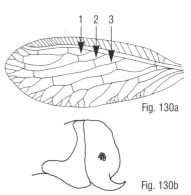

Fig. 130a

Fig. 130b

–   Four (Fig. 131a) or five (Fig. 131b) branches to the radial vein. Fore wing membrane brownish, or yellowish tinged and marked with darker brown. Hind wing never with dark marks at the apex – usually unmarked apart from the line of cross-veins. Wing span (across both wings) 15 mm or more. Tip of male abdomen like Figs. 131c or d in side view 2

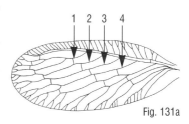

Fig. 131a

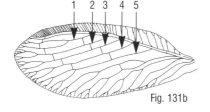

Fig. 131b

Fig. 131c

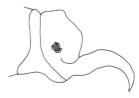

Fig. 131d

2   Four branches to the radial vein of the fore wing and these wings narrow and
     rounded at apex (Fig. 132a). Wings usually a reddish brown colour when fresh. Tip
     of male abdomen with a small, narrow horizontal spike suspended from the last
     segment (Fig. 132b) in side view ....*Micromus angulatus*

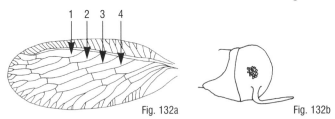

Fig. 132a   Fig. 132b

–   Five branches to the radial vein of the fore wing and these wings broad in
     appearance with less rounded tips (Fig. 133a). Fore wings usually yellowish brown.
     Tip of male abdomen with downwards curving 'cat's claws' (Fig. 133b) ....
     ....*Micromus paganus*

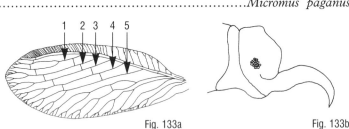

Fig. 133a   Fig. 133b

NOTE: Occasionally, examples of *M. paganus* can be found with only four branches to the radial vein of the fore wing, whilst there are reputed to be examples of *M. variegatus* with only two branches. If a specimen does not key out satisfactorily here on wing characters, the answer obtained by looking at the tip of the male abdomen takes preference. There are no discernible differences in the shape of the tip of the female abdomen. In reality, all three species are distinctive and can be very easily recognised on sight after a little experience has been gained.

Key K

SPECIES OF *SYMPHEROBIUS*

Recognition features: Small sized brown lacewings with a recurrent humeral vein (Fig. 122). Subcostal vein continues to wing tip and does not fuse with vein R (though cross-veins may be present). Radio-medial cross-vein (RMCV; Figs. 134, 135) apparently with a gap at the centre (actually caused by lack of pigmentation). Four British species, and a further three in Europe, of which one, *S. klapaleki*, could perhaps occur in the south-east, although this is considered unlikely.

1   Two branches to the radial vein of the fore wing (Fig. 134). Veins of the fore wings uniformly dark OR alternating light and dark bands 2

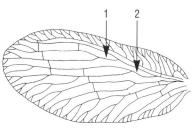

Fig. 134

–   Three branches to the radial vein of the fore wing (Fig. 135). Veins of the forewings uniformly dark, never with alternating light and dark bands **3**

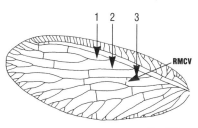

NOTE: I have a specimen of *S. elegans* in my own collection with three branches to the radial vein in the left fore wing and only two in the right. If other examples occur these should be checked against the other characters given in couplets 2 - 3 of this key.

Fig. 135

2   Veins of fore wings uniformly dark. Wing membrane bordering the longitudinal veins of the fore wings, at least in the basal half of the wing, transparent. Remaining wing membranes of fore wings marbled with brown on a transparent background. Thorax usually uniformly dark viewed from above. Tip of male abdomen in side view as Fig. 136 ....*S. elegans*

–   Veins of fore wings with alternating dark and light streaks. Membranes of fore wings marked with small clear patches on a pale brown background, these clear patches being centred on the pale streaks of the veins. Thorax, viewed from above, usually with a pale centre. Tip of male abdomen in side view as Fig. 137 ....*S. pygmaeus*

3   Fore wing membrane transparent with no darkening around the cross-veins. Tip of male abdomen in side view as Fig. 138 ...*S. fuscescens*

–   Fore wing membrane transparent but with distinct darkening in the vicinity of the cross-veins. All antennal segments, including scape and pedicel dark brown in colour ⋆. Tip of male abdomen in side view as Fig. 139 ....*S. pellucidus*

NOTE: ⋆ If *S. klapaleki* is present in Britain, it would key out here with *S. pellucidus*, and from which it may be distinguished by the clear yellow-brown colouration of the first two antennal segments (scape and pedicel), contrasting with the dark brown colour of the rest of the antennae. Tip of male abdomen in side view as Fig. 142.

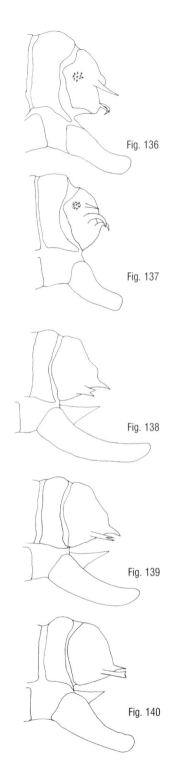

Fig. 136

Fig. 137

Fig. 138

Fig. 139

Fig. 140

KEY L

SPECIES OF *HEMEROBIUS*

Recognition features: Brown lacewings with a recurrent humeral vein and the basal cross-vein between veins R and M in the fore wing situated basal to the first fork of vein M or sometimes coinciding with the fork. Confusion is most likely with the genus *Wesmaelius* in which this cross-vein meets vein M after its fork (Fig. 129) and from which male specimens may be distinguished by the shape of the tip of abdomen in lateral view and females by their complete lack of the anal plates present in *Wesmaelius*. There are 12 British species. A further four are currently known from the rest of Europe though they are all southern and are rather unlikely to occur in Britain.

1   In the forewing, the cross-vein MCCV (see Fig. 141), is either completely colourless OR if black, then the membrane of the wing immediately surrounding this cross-vein absolutely lacks dark clouding. Whole **membrane** of fore wing is generally un-marked – any markings at all are extremely pale and are generally not visible to the naked eye so that the wing appears quite unmarked other than on the veins **2**

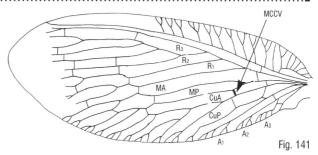

Fig. 141

–   In the forewing, the cross-vein MCCV (see Fig. 141) is dark AND the wing **membrane** surrounding this cross-vein is shaded darker than the rest of the wing membrane, even if only narrowly so against the vein. The wing membrane as a whole usually bears one or more areas of darker shading that are visible to the unaided eye (except in some teneral specimens) **4**

2   In the forewing, MCCV (see Fig. 141) is completely colourless. The longitudinal veins of the forewing bear dark spots, the length of which is about the same as the width of the vein on which they sit (Fig. 142). The majority of the wing hairs which arise from these dark spots are dark. Head, including face, brown, the face tending to be darker in female specimens ....*H. nitidulus*

Fig. 142

NOTE: If your specimen has been an obvious orange-coloured pterostigma it is more likely to be *H. stigma* (see couplet 4).

–   In the forewing, MCCV (see Fig. 141) is dark. The longitudinal veins of the fore wing bear dashes, each at least twice as long as the width of the vein on which they sit (Fig. 143). The wing hairs arising from these dark dashes are predominantly pale **3**

Fig. 143

3   In the fore wing, the wing membrane is uniformly transparent, usually with yellowish reflections, apart from occasional very faint V-shaped markings around some of the dark dashes on the longitudinal veins, not at all easily seen by the un-aided eye and often absent ....*H. micans*

–   In the fore wing, the wing membrane bears some dark patches in the rear half of the wing, especially towards the base, so that the wing membrane is not uniformly colourless (try looking at various angles without a microscope if uncertain, but the markings are usually obvious) ....*H. lutescens*

4   Top of thorax the same brown colour as the sides; no hint of a pale dorsal thoracic stripe. Wings with characteristic orange-coloured pterostigmata ....*H. stigma*

NOTE: *H. stigma* bears a superficial resemblence to *H. nitidulus*. However, *H. nitidulus* never has obvious orange-coloured pterostigmata.

–   Top of thorax paler than sides **5**

5   Front of face shining glossy black across the full
width. Internal genitalia of male in caudal view
(viewed from directly behind) like Fig. 144 ....
....*H. atrifrons*

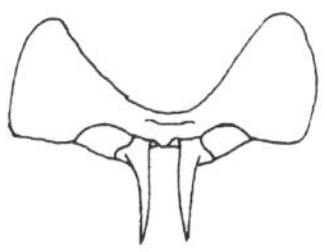

Fig. 144

—   Front of face not glossy black across full width,
though sometimes black at the sides. Always some
brown areas **6**

NOTE: Some examples of *H. pini*, keyed out later in couplet 10, can also have faces which are considerably darkened, though usually this is not
entirely glossy black and does not extend fully across the width of the face, usually leaving a brown centre. If there is any doubt, however, it will
be necessary to examine the genitalia of a male example (see Figs. 144, 145a-c). Note also that the common species of *Wesmaelius* also have
a glossy black face , so if you are in any doubt recheck Key I, couplet 7.

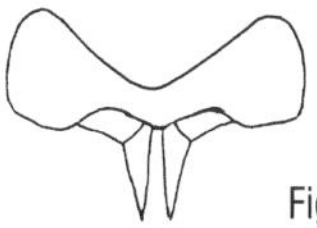

Fig. 145a

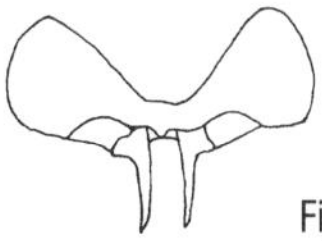

Fig. 145b

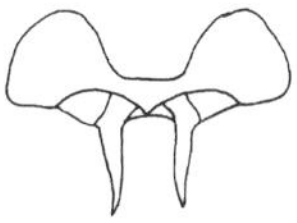

Fig. 145c

6   Basal cross-vein connecting veins Sc and R (Fig.
146) is entirely pale or only slightly darkened at
the end that joins vein R **7**

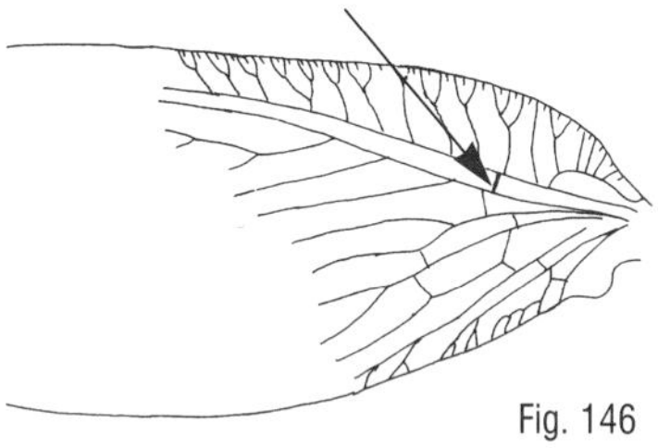

Fig. 146

—   Basal cross-vein connecting veins Sc and R is dark, usually black, for all or most of
its length **8**

7   Hind margin of fore wing with three or four dark marks, including a long narrow
     one at the point where the veinlets of vein A1 meet the hind margin, so that all these
     veinlets are dark (Fig. 147a). Wing membrane in the front half of the fore wing
     largely unmarked. Longitudinal veins of the fore wing largely pale, only marked
     with the occasional dark streak or darkened at the forks. Costal space of fore wing
     wider in the basal third than other species; measured at the widest point of the
     costal space, along a line at right angles to the subcostal vein, the ratio of the width
     of the subcostal space divided by the distance across the whole wing is 0.3 or greater
     (Fig. 147b). Tip of male abdomen as in Fig. 147c ....*H. marginatus*

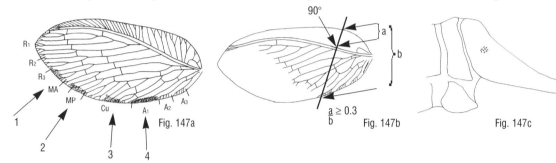

Fig. 147a   Fig. 147b   Fig. 147c

–   Fore wing markings different. If a dark mark is present on the hind margin in the
     region of vein A1 then it does not include all the veinlets of A1 in the dark area and
     it extends forwards away from the hind margin beyond vein A1 as a smudge on the
     membrane (Fig. 148a). Longitudinal veins of fore wings not almost entirely pale,
     but furnished with dark marks at much more regular intervals. Costal space of
     forewing measured as above narrower, the ratio being 0.25 or less (Fig. 148a). Tip
     of male abdomen as in Fig. 148b ....*H. lutescens*

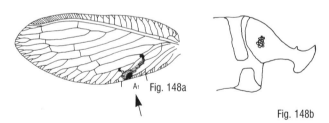

A₁   Fig. 148a

Fig. 148b

8   Hind margin of fore wing uniformly shaded greyish or brownish, so that there are
     absolutely no transparent areas that connect with the hind margin of the wing. The
     remainder of the fore wing is generally transparent with or without areas of shading
     ....**9**

–   Hind margin of fore wing is not uniformly shaded, and there are always some
     transparent areas of membrane connecting with the hind margin. In some cases
     these may be very small regularly spaced 'windows' so look carefully under a
     magnification of x20 or greater and view at different angles to be certain **11**

9   Outer series of gradate veins in the fore wing (Fig. 149a) colourless or nearly so; when viewed with the naked eye, these veins are clearly colourless when compared to the inner series. Internal genitalia of male in caudal view (viewed directly from behind) like Fig. 149b ....*H. fenestratus*

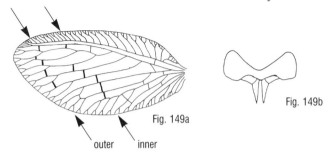

Fig. 149a

Fig. 149b

outer   inner

NOTE: A recent colonist, so far known only from East Kent but likely to spread. Records will require confirmation.

–   Outer series of gradate veins in the fore wing (see above) are darkened, so that to the naked eye both the outer and inner series appear darkened more or less equally dark **10**

10   Inner and outer series of gradate veins in the fore wing are closely parallel (Fig. 150a). Internal genitalia of male in caudal view (viewed directly from behind) like Fig. 150b ....*H. contumax*

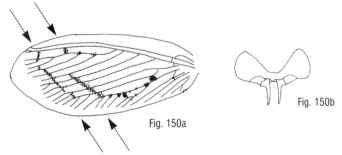

Fig. 150b

Fig. 150a

NOTE: Regarded as possibly extinct in Britain. Records will require confirmation.

–   Inner and outer series of gradate veins in the fore wing are not closely parallel, diverging towards the front margin of the wing (Fig. 151a). Internal genitalia of male in caudal view (viewed directly from behind) like Fig. 151b ....*H. pini*

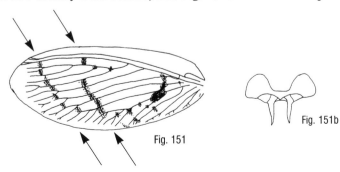

Fig. 151b

Fig. 151

11 Wing span, across both wings and the body, usually greater than 20 mm – at any rate greater than 18 mm. Inner series of gradate veins in the fore wing are usually arranged as a straight line (Fig. 152a). Scape (the large first segment) of antenna **usually** with a dark longitudinal line on the front outer corner (Fig. 152b). Membrane of fore wing uniformly shaded grey on the hind margin but with small, transparent 'windows' at regular intervals. General appearance is of a largish, narrow-winged grey species. Wings never with a yellowish reflection at any angle of view and never a rich red-brown colour ....*H. simulans*

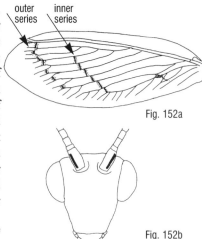

Fig. 152a

Fig. 152b

NOTE: *Hemerobius fenestratus* (couplet 9) may also have a dark line on the antennal scape but the overall appearance of the two species is totally different.

– Wing span, across both wings and the body, almost always less than 18 mm – at any rate less than 20 mm. Inner series of gradate veins in the fore wing usually angled at the middle (Fig. 153). Scape (the large first segment) of antenna usually without a dark longitudinal line on the front outer corner (a faint line may sometimes be present in *H. humulinus* but it is absent from the other species). Hind margin of fore wing different, with much larger areas of transparent membrane connecting with the hind edge. The general appearance is of a smaller, shorter-winged insect, either a rich reddish brown colour, or clear wings with a pattern of spots and shading, sometimes with a yellowish reflection **12**

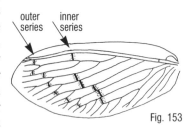

Fig. 153

12 Fore wings a rich reddish-brown colour, the longitudinal veins heavily and closely marked. Wing membrane surrounding the dark marks on the longitudinal veins with clear 'V-shaped' marks, the apex of the 'V' pointing towards the wing base ....*H. perelegans*

– Fore wings pale, lightly and more loosely marked with grey or pale brown patterning, never a rich reddish brown colour. Wings may or may not have yellowish reflections. Any 'V-shaped' marks on the wing membrane are pale grey and do not stand out; mostly they are rather indistinct **13**

13 Tip of male abdomen as Fig. 154a in side view. Female with last segment of abdomen pronounced (Fig. 154b) ....*H. lutescens*

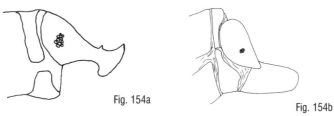

Fig. 154a

Fig. 154b

NOTE: *H. lutescens* is keyed out here in addition to couplets 3 and 7 because on very rare occasions examples occur in which the cross-vein between Sc and R is darkened. Most examples would have this vein pale and key out in couplet 7 (occasionally at couplet 3). In reality, however, *H. lutescens* and *H. humulinus* can be separated 'by eye' on their overall appearance after a little practice.

— Tip of male abdomen as Figure 155a,b (Two variations are shown of the male abdomen. Because the tip of the abdomen is 3-dimensional, tilting the specimen slightly will alter the precise shape of the last segment as it appears to the eye). Female with last segment of abdomen not particularly pronounced (Fig. 155c) ....*H. humulinus*

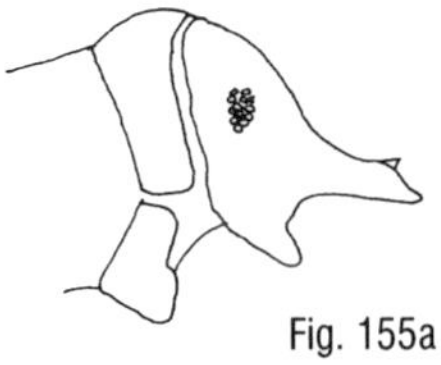

Fig. 155a

Fig. 155b

Fig. 155c

KEY M

SPECIES OF *WESMAELIUS*

Recognition features: Brown lacewings with a recurrent humeral vein and in which the basal cross-vein between veins R and M in the fore wing reaches vein M after the fork of vein M as in Fig. 144, unlike members of the genus *Hemerobius* in which the cross vein lands on M before M forks (Fig. 143a). Males of *Wesmaelius* have tips of the abdomen quite different to males of *Hemerobius* (refer to Figs. 162-165), whilst females have anal plates on the ventral surface of the tip of the abdomen (Figs. 166-169) unlike females of *Hemerobius* which do not (Fig. 128b). There are eight species of *Wesmaelius* recorded in Britain, though one of these is regarded as being extinct. A number of other species are present in Europe; none is considered likely to occur undetected in Britain.

1   Radial vein in fore wing with four branches (check both wings) (Fig. 156a). Tip of male abdomen triangular in shape (Figs. 156b,c); tip of female abdomen with long narrow process (Figs. 156d,e) ....(subgenus *Wesmaelius*) **2**

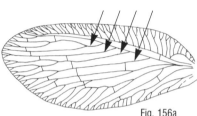

Fig. 156a

Fig. 156b   Fig. 156c

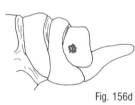

Fig. 156d

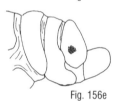

Fig. 156e

–   Radial vein of fore wing with only three branches as in Fig. 157a (check both wings). Tip of male abdomen not triangular, but variously shaped (Figs. 157b,c); tip of female abdomen with the final segment rounded and not markedly pronounced (Fig. 157d) ....(subgenus *Kimminsia*) **3**

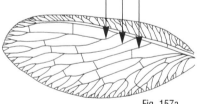

Fig. 157a

Fig. 157b

Fig. 157c

Fig. 157d

2   Thorax unicolorous pale orangey-brown, without
    a pale stripe on top. Longitudinal veins in fore
    wing pale with darker spots – the length of most of
    these spots being only around 1.5 to 2 times the
    width of the vein they are situated on. Fore wing
    membrane clear with pale 'v-shaped' marks
    centred on the dark vein spots and with the angle
    of the 'V' pointing towards the wing base. Tip of
    male abdomen as in Fig. 158a; anal plates on
    ventral surface of female as Fig. 158b ....
    ....*W. concinnus*

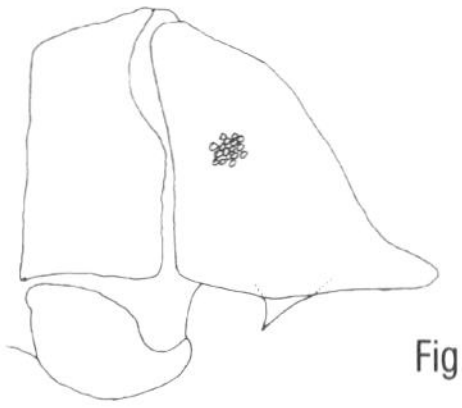

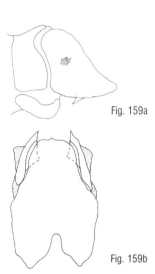

Fig. 158a

Fig. 158b

–   Thorax dark brown with a pale dorsal stripe.
    Longitudinal veins of fore wing pale with dark
    streaks, the length of most of these streaks being
    far in excess of twice the width of the vein on
    which they are situated. Fore wing membrane
    clear with darkish markings centred on the dark
    vein streaks, resembling the 'V-shapes' described
    for W. concinnus above but broader and running
    into each other in some areas Tip of male
    abdomen as in Fig. 159a; anal plates on ventral
    surface of female as Fig. 159b ...*W. quadrifasciatus*

Fig. 159a

Fig. 159b

COUPLETS 3-7 SUBGENUS *KIMMINSIA*

With few exceptions, the remaining species are impossible to separate 'by eye' and I have been unable to find any venational character that is constant in all examples examined. Specimens of *W. (K.) mortoni* (considered extinct in Britain) and *W. (K.) balticus* (a local and rather rare species) can be recognised using the key in most cases but identifications should always be confirmed by examining the genitalia (see page 265). The remaining species can only be reliably identified by examining the genitalia and so there is little point in repeating here the traditional but unreliable wing characters of earlier keys. Specimens preserved in alcohol or other fluid can usually (though not always) be identified without further treatment, as can pinned, dry males of our two widespread and common species *subnebulosus* and *nervosus* (= *betulinus*); other males and all pinned, dry female specimens will normally require clearing before examination (see page 265).

3   Thorax uniformly pale orange-brown 4

–   Thorax dark brown, with or without a pale central stripe 5

4   Longitudinal veins of fore wings marked with regularly spaced dark spots. Tip of male abdomen as in Fig. 160a. Female anal plate as in Fig. 160b. ...*W. (K.) mortoni*

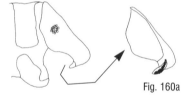

Fig. 160a

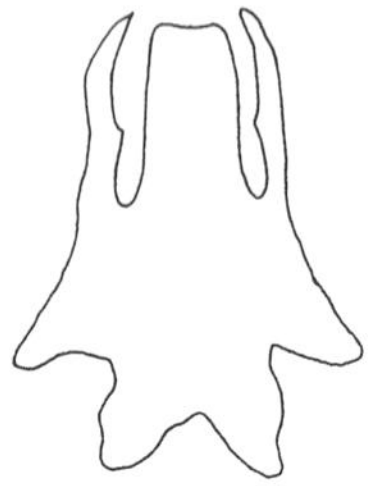

NOTE: Characters are based on Continental specimens!

Fig. 160b

–   Longitudinal veins of fore wings clear, without dark spots. Tip of male abdomen as in Fig. 187a. Female anal plate as in Fig. 187b ....*W. (K.) balticus*

Fig. 161a

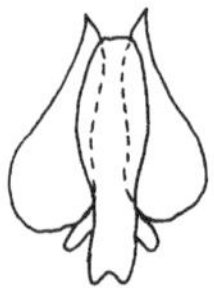

Fig. 161b

NOTE: Confusion is possible between W. balticus and Hemerobius micans which is superficially similar - check the R-M cross-vein character carefully (Key I, couplet 7 on page 234). Specimens of H. micans from coastal sand dune areas, especially where trees are absent, should always be checked by reference to the genitalia of the male or the anal plates of the female.

5   Males (tip of abdomen as in Figs. 162-165) **6**

–   Females (tip of abdomen as in Figs. 166-169) **7**

READ FOUR CHOICES

6   Tip of abdomen furnished with two 'fish hooks' (Fig. 162). Turn the specimen to view from different angles to be certain. ....
.....................................*W. (K.) subnebulosus*

Fig. 162

OR Tip of abdomen as in Fig. 163 ....
.............................*W. (K.) nervosus (=betulinus)*

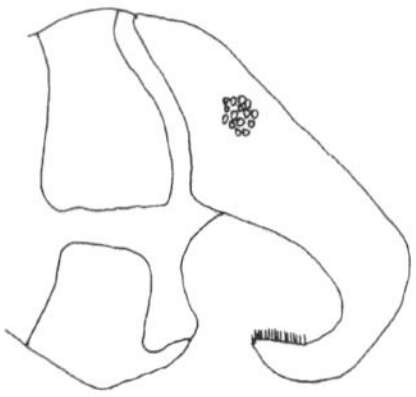

Fig. 163

OR Tip of abdomen as in Fig. 164 ...*W. (K.) malladai*

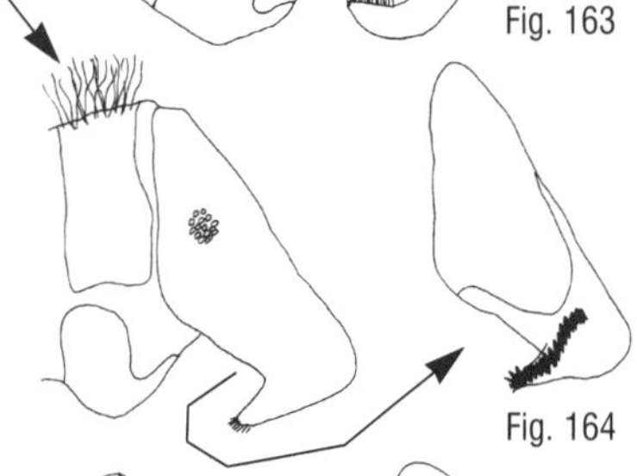

Fig. 164

OR Tip of abdomen as in Fig. 165 ......*W. (K.) ravus*

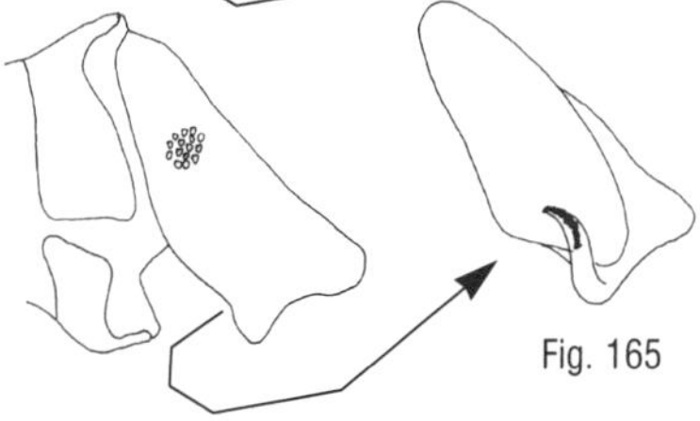

Fig. 165

READ FOUR CHOICES

7   Anal plates as in Fig. 166 ...*W. (K.) subnebulosus*

OR Anal plates as in Fig. 167 ....
.............................*W. (K.) nervosus (=betulinus)*

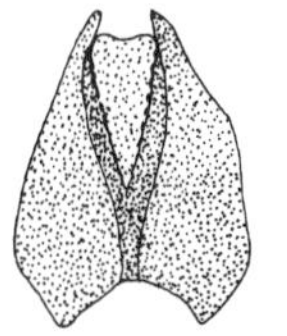

OR Anal plates as in Fig. 168 ....*W. (K.) malladai*

OR Anal plates as in Fig. 169 ....*W. (K.) ravus*

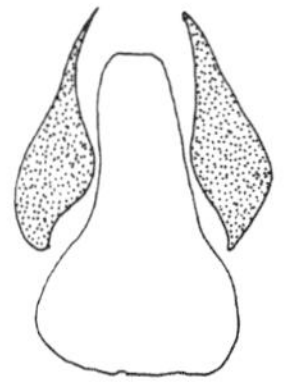

NOTE: In freshly emerged females of *W. nervosus* the smaller pair of anal plates may not be fully developed and this may lead to incorrect identification of this widespread and very common species as *W. malladai*, which is restricted to the Scottish Highlands.

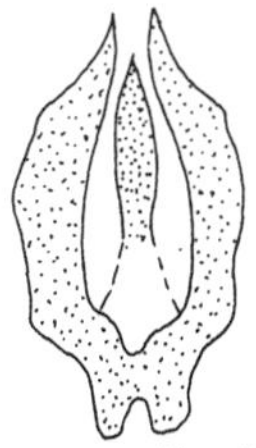

Fig. 166   Fig. 167

Fig. 168   Fig. 169

APPENDIX 1

NOTES ON THE SPECIES

The approximate distributions of species are given below, together with other notes where appropriate, so that entomologists using the keys may know if a species is recorded outside its expected range. Whilst the relatively poor coverage of most of Britain and Ireland outside the south and south-east means that the known distributions are little more than provisional, the author would nevertheless be keen to examine specimens well outside their expected geographical range. The recorded flight periods for adults are indicated in Plant (1994). However, these are likely to be extended in many cases as our knowledge increases, and so I regard it as misleading to give them here.

RAPHIDIOPTERA – THE SNAKE FLIES

The snake flies are seldom encountered but this is probably more to do with them spending their adult lives at the tops of trees than anything else. They are best found by sweeping bushes and other vegetation near woodland after very strong winds or by beating trees from a ladder (in areas where deer shooting takes place, the shooting platforms erected in trees are worth utilising to reach the upper branches). The larvae are predatory on beetle larvae and probably Diptera larvae, and live under loose bark where they are frequently mistaken for beetle larvae themselves; there is as yet no reliable means of separating them from each other apart from breeding them through. There is a single British family, Raphidiidae, containing four British species in four genera as follows.

Atlantoraphidia maculicollis (Stephens, 1836)
Widely spread in England, Wales and Scotland, but not yet recorded from Ireland. Associated with *Pinus* and most common in the south.

Phaeostigma notata (Fabricius, 1781)
Widespread in association with deciduous *Quercus* in England and Wales, but not recorded from Scotland or Ireland.

Subilla confinis (Stephens, 1836)
Widespread but local in central, eastern and south-eastern England only. Its specific tree associations are not clear.

Xanthostigma xanthostigma (Schummel, 1832)
Widespread and locally common in England, mostly in the Midlands and East Anglia. Very localised in Wales and apparently absent from Scotland and Ireland. Its specific tree associations are not clear.

MEGALOPTERA – THE ALDER FLIES

The alder flies are familiar insects of waterside vegetation early in the year and it is, principally, their aquatic larvae which separates the Megaloptera from the Raphidioptera. Eggs are laid on emergent vegetation, rarely on other objects, and the hatched larvae fall into the water. The larval stage usually lasts for two years before pupation in a cocoon about a centimetre deep in waterside debris. Emergence of the adults is usually synchronised, and so huge numbers may be present at a given point in time. The three British species fall into a single family, the Sialidae, which is represented by a single genus – *Sialis.*

Sialis fuliginosa Pictet, 1836
Widespread but rather local in Britain, but not yet noted from Ireland. All records relate to flowing water, though torrents appear unsuitable.

Sialis lutaria (Linnaeus, 1758)
Widespread and common throughout Britain but apparently local in Ireland. This is our commonest species and is to be found in most static water bodies, including static backwaters on rivers, provided there is a covering of bottom mud and some emergent vegetation.

Sialis nigripes Pictet, 1865
Widespread but evidently quite local in England, Wales, Scotland and Ireland, though certainly under-recorded. It was not detected as a British species until 1976 (Barnard, 1977). Most records come from calcareous waters but there are others from acidic rivers in Wales. A note of water pH value would be a useful accompaniment to any record!

NEUROPTERA

Formerly referred to as Planipennia, this includes all the true lacewings. There are currently 65 British species known in six families, presented alphabetically as follows:

CHRYSOPIDAE – THE GREEN LACEWINGS

Chrysopa abbreviata Curtis, 1834
A rather local species of coastal sand dunes with marram grass, where the larvae probably feed on aphids specific to the marram. Probably under-recorded.

Chrysopa commata Kis & Ujhelyi, 1965
This species was split from *C. phyllochroma* in 1965, and is now proving to be the more common of the pair. Widespread south of a line from Liverpool to the Humber, but curiously absent from most of Wales. Continental specimens often have a dark mark on the inner face of the antennal scape, but this is absent from almost all British specimens. The pattern of spots and lunules on the top of the head is extremely variable and unreliable as a determining character on its own. Voucher specimens should be retained where possible.

Chrysopa dorsalis Burmeister, 1839
Extremely local and usually rare, probably genuinely so. There is some evidence that south coast records may be of immigrants; the species is widespread in most of Europe and we are probably on the extreme edge of its range here. It is associated with pines.

Chrysopa pallens (Rambur, 1838)
Formerly known as *C. septempunctata* this is a common species in England and Wales, but not yet recorded from Scotland or Ireland. It is a regular in mercury vapour light traps in many suburban gardens.

Chrysopa perla (Linnaeus, 1758)
A widespread and very common species, especially in scrubby grassland and woodland edge habitats, in England, Wales and the southern half of Scotland.

Chrysopa phyllochroma Wesmael, 1841
Local and rare in England and Wales, with all recent records emanating from light traps. Because of earlier confusion with *C. commata* we know little of its past history in Britain. It is perhaps under-recorded, but voucher material should be retained wherever possible.

Chrysoperla carnea (Stephens) & *Chrysoperla lucasina* (Lacroix)
Until as recently as this year, 1997, opinions have differed a great deal over just how many species are involved in the *Chrysoperla carnea* complex. Current opinion favours two – *C. carnea* sensu stricto and *C. lucasina*, both of which appear, on the very limited data available, to be widespread and common in Britain, though we have no information on these segregate species for Ireland. However, a great many specimens will be encountered that do not quite fit either of these two species and these will just have to be recorded as *C. carnea* group for the time being. The aggregate species affects most of the world and is extaordinarily abundant (most British green lacewings encountered will be this 'species') and it may simply be that we have just one species which is actively evolving into several species at the present moment in historical time.

Chrysopidia ciliata (Wesmael, 1841)
Widespread and locally common throughout the British Isles, possibly having an affinity with oaks and other deciduous trees.

Cunctochrysa albolineata (Killington, 1935)
Widespread and common throughout the British Isles, in association with deciduous trees and shrubs.

Cunctochrysa bellifontensis Leraut, 1988
The existence of this as a valid species is not universally accepted, and some regard it as a variety of *C. albolineata* in which the basal cross-vein of the fore wing is black. Until the matter is adequately resolved, it makes sense to segregate records and retain voucher specimens. It is so far recorded from a pine plantation in Suffolk, from a woodland in Buckinghamshire and from a light trap on an urban rooftop in east London (Plant, 1993). All British records appear to relate to females.

Dichochrysa flavifrons (Brauer, 1850)
Widespread and very common in England and Wales, though rather scarce in the north of England, absent from Scotland and known only from a single very old record in Ireland. In recent years it seems to have increased in numbers dramatically and extended its range northwards.

Dichochrysa prasina (Burmeister, 1839)
Another widespread and common species in England and Wales, also recorded on the eastern seaboard of Ireland but not at all in Scotland. It was, formerly, incorrectly regarded as a subspecies of *D. ventralis* and its former history in the British Isles is unclear since records referring simply to ventralis cannot be reliably assigned to either species unless a voucher specimen is available.

Dichochrysa ventralis (Curtis, 1834)
Widespread and common throughout the British Isles, but very local and scarce in Ireland and Scotland. Associated with both deciduous and coniferous trees. Comments under the previous species also apply here.

Nineta flava (Scopoli, 1763)
Widespread and common in woodlands throughout the British Isles, perhaps associated with oak.

Nineta inpunctata (Reuter, 1894)
Known from a single female taken at mercury vapour light at a woodland in North Essex during 1989. It is only rarely captured in Europe and usually in ones or twos, which may suggest a secretive, perhaps arboreal, habit that renders it under-recorded. It may, therefore, be an ovelooked resident in this country, but records will require confirmation. It is associated with mixed scrub and woodland in Europe and the Essex record fits this pattern.

Nineta vittata (Wesmael, 1841)
Widespread and quite common in all areas of the British Isles, associated with a range of deciduous trees.

Nothochrysa capitata (Fabricius, 1793)
Widespread and local in England and Wales, scarce in Scotland and so far absent from Ireland. Typically associated with pine, but several records are associated with the tops of oak trees.

Nothochrysa fulviceps (Stephens, 1836)
There is one record from Cumbria in 1995, but otherwise this lacewing has not been recorded in the British Isles since 1958. It is common in parts of Europe where it comes to light traps in number. It is strictly associated with the tops of mature oak trees and so may just persist undetected in several areas. All records will require confirmation.

CONIOPTERYGIDAE – THE WAX FLIES

A much neglected family of lacewings on account of their very small size and the need to examine the genitalia to be certain of a correct identification. Lack of attention to this latter point has, in the past, led to many erroneous statements. One good example is that in Fraser (1959) which states that *Coniopteryx borealis* is known in Britain from only two specimens taken in Scotland; genitalia examination of museum specimens indicates that this was untrue even then, with several examples from all over Britain. Both *C. esbenpeterseni* and *C. lentiae* have remained undetected for over a hundred years, whilst *Semidalis pseudouncinata* could not have been detected as a recent colonist if one had assumed that there was only one species of *Semidalis* in Britain. There are doubtless further Coniopterygid species to be found in Britain and the ranges of the existing species may all be expanded considerably.

Coniopterygidae may be collected by sweeping and beating vegetation; using a black net makes finding them easier. They also come to light traps and to house lights but can be hard to see on a white-painted kitchen ceiling. Females cannot be identified on present knowledge. All species are best preserved in alcohol or some other fluid medium and the specimens should always be kept as vouchers.

Aleuropteryx juniperi Ohm, 1968
Extremely rare, known from only two localities, both in the south of England (Ward, 1970), and only known to breed at one of these, though it has not been looked for here since 1965! The larvae are associated with juniper *Juniperus communis*. Beating native juniper in the south of England with a black net may reveal additional localities. Records will require confirmation.

Coniopteryx (Coniopteryx) borealis Tjeder, 1930
Widespread and very common throughout England, wales and Scotland; perhaps our commonest species.

Coniopteryx (Metaconiopteryx) esbenpeterseni Tjeder, 1930
First recognised in Britain in 1987 (Hynd & Plant, 1991) this species has been overlooked as a resident; specimens in museums date back to 1878. It is proving to be widespread and common in England, south of about Manchester, though it could easily be found further north as it is present in Norway. Since it is principally known from light traps, its habitat preferences are unknown.

Coniopteryx (Metaconiopteryx) lentiae Aspöck & Aspöck, 1964
Like the preceding species, this has been an overlooked resident, not detected until 1986 (Hynd, 1989). It is less widespread, and rather more local than *C. esbenpeterseni*, with records coming from the south and south-east of England. Its habitat requirements are equally uncertain.

Coniopteryx (Coniopteryx) pygmaea Enderlein, 1906, nec auctt.
Günther, (1993) has shown that this is the correct name for the species we have referred to until recently as *C. parthenia* (Navas & Marcet, 1910). The European species referred to as *C. pygmaea* auctt. is actually *C. holzeli* Aspöck, 1964. It is widespread but very local and scarce in England, Wales and Scotland.

Coniopteryx (Coniopteryx) tineiformis Curtis, 1834
Widespread and quite common in England, Wales and Scotland. Present, but grossly under-recorded in Ireland.

Conwentzia pineticola Enderlein, 1905
Widespread in England, local and rare in Scotland (Fifeshire), and not yet recorded in Wales or Ireland. It is strictly associated with pine trees, though very few data are available concerning which species of Pinus.

Conwentzia psociformis (Curtis, 1834)
Widespread and common in England, local but probably under-recorded in Wales, rare and certainly under-recorded in Scotland and Ireland. It is associated with deciduous trees and bushes.

Helicoconis hirtinervis Tjeder, 1960/*lutea* (Wallengren, 1871)
The genus *Helicoconis* is reliably recorded in Britain from a single example of a brachypterous female collected on the ground under heather, near the coast in Sutherland during 1993. Although females can not be reliably identified it is probably *H. hirtinervis* as the wing veins bear hairs and the vestigial hind wing appears wrong for *lutea*. Earlier records of *H. lutea* from Britain are known to be erroneous (Plant, 1991). Thus, though the genus is recorded in Britain, the species is yet to be discovered. Two other species, *H. pseudolutea* and *H. egglini*, are known from southern Europe, but brachyptery is not known in these. Thus, the keys include *H. lutea* and *H. hirtinervis* but all records will require confirmation.

Parasemidalis fuscipennis (Reuter, 1894)
Widespread but very local in England, south to a line from Liverpool to Whitby, with a single record from Wales. Examples have been taken from pine, oak and reedmace (*Typha latifolia*).

Semidalis aleyrodiformis (Stephens, 1836)
Widespread but local in England, though curiously absent from Wales and very rare in Scotland. Apparently absent from Ireland.

Semidalis pseudouncinata Meinander, 1963
This is a recent arrival in Britain (Plant, 1992), associated with *Cupressus*, *Thuja* and other similar ornamental conifer trees. It probably arrived here under its own steam, rather than as an introduction, since though the trees have been imported for several years, the insect has only slowly expanded northwards across Europe in the wake. It is so far recorded only from the south-east but is likely to spread widely and may already be overlooked in many parts of Britain and Ireland.

HEMEROBIIDAE – THE BROWN LACEWINGS

Drepanepteryx phalaenoides (Linnaeus, 1758)
Most records relate to woodlands, but there are records from other habitats. The distribution is somewhat disjunct, with centres in the south-east and the north of England and isolated recordings in the Midlands, Wales, Scotland and Ireland. It has been suggested that this species may hibernate as an adult, though there is no real evidence to support this at present.

Hemerobius atrifrons McLachlan, 1868
Widespread but local in England, Wales and Scotland, strictly associated with larch trees *Larix decidua*.

Hemerobius contumax Tjeder
There are a very few old records from Surrey, Hampshire, Buckinghamshire and Sussex, plus an unconfirmed record from Yorkshire, but this insect has not been recorded in Britain since 1952 and is presumed to be extinct here. It is supposedly associated with pine trees. Any records will require confirmation.

Hemerobius fenestratus Tjeder, 1932
Added to the British list in 1986 (Plant & Barnard, 1988), this species is known in Britain only from three specimens from two localities, both in East Kent. It is confined to pine trees and is almost certainly a recent colonist, and so has the potential to spread. Records will require confirmation.

Hemerobius humulinus Linnaeus, 1761
One of the commonest of the brown lacewings, widely spread in a variety of habitats throughout Britain and Ireland

Hemerobius lutescens Fabricius, 1793
A common and widespread species throughout the whole of Britain and Ireland in a variety of habitats.

Hemerobius marginatus Stephens, 1836
A widespread but apparently local species in most of Britain and Ireland. Records indicate an association with birch, hazel and alder.

Hemerobius micans Olivier, 1792
Widespread and common in Britain and Ireland wherever there are oak trees of any reasonable age.

Hemerobius nitidulus Fabricius, 1777
Widespread but rather local throughout Britain and also sparingly recorded from Ireland. It is associated with pines.

Hemerobius perelegans Stephens, 1836
Very local and apparently rare, recorded from the north of England and northern Scotland only, where it is apparently associated with mature birch (*Betula*) trees in rocky upland areas.

Hemerobius pini Stephens, 1836
Widespread and local, but locally quite common in Britain, with a single record from the east side of Ireland. As the name suggests it is associated with pines, particularly Scots pine (*Pinus sylvestris*).

Hemerobius simulans Walker, 1853
Widespread but local throughout Britain, and probably also throughout Ireland. It is probably under-recorded because of its late appearance in the year, with specimens still in evidence in October and November. Supposedly confined to larch (*Larix decidua*) but perhaps also able to thrive on spruce (*Picea* sp.) or even on pines.

Hemerobius stigma Stephens, 1836
One of the commonest species in pine woodlands, particularly associated with Scots pine *Pinus sylvestris*. It is widespread and common throughout the British Isles.

Megalomus hirtus (Linnaeus, 1761)
Confined to a single site in Edinburgh where it is under no immediate threat but is clearly vulnerable both to land use change and over-collecting. There are old records from several sites in Kincardineshire. It is almost certainly associated with wood sage (*Teucrium scorodonia*) on rocky hill-sides and under-cliffs and rarely takes to flight, so could be overlooked elsewhere. An old record from Devon is an error.

Micromus angulatus (Stephens, 1836)
Widespread but very local and usually scarce in England, Wales and Ireland. The habitat requirements are unclear, being recorded from both calcareous and acid grassland, scrub habitats and suburban gardens.

Micromus paganus (Linnaeus, 1767)
A widespread and very common species throughout the British Isles in a wide variety of habitats. This is one of the few species present in upland areas and in some Highland regions is the dominant species.

Micromus variegatus (Fabricius, 1793)
A widespread and quite common insect in England and Wales, with several records in Ireland, but becoming localised in the north of England and rare in Scotland. It readily comes to house lights during August but otherwise is a species of dense herbage.

Psectra diptera (Burmeister, 1836)
There are two forms of this lacewing, occurring in either sex, sometimes with both forms in the same population. In the micropterous form the hind wings are vestigial and the insect is probably incapable of flight. In the macropterous form all four wings are fully developed and the insect does indeed fly. It seems to have a close association with grass tussocks and probably feeds on root aphids. It is widespread and under-recorded in England, Wales and Scotland, with a few records from Ireland. It is most frequently encountered in pitfall traps or water traps, although the fully-winged forms come to light traps. Records should include a note on which form was involved.

Sympherobius (Sympherobius) elegans (Stephens, 1836)
Widespread but rather local in central and eastern England, with a few isolated records in south Wales, but so far absent from the rest of Wales, the West Country, north-west England, Scotland and Ireland. It is almost certainly under-recorded in some of these areas. It is associated with deciduous woodland but any specific tree-insect relationship is not known.

Sympherobius (Niremberge) fuscescens (Wallengren, 1863)
Confined to scots pine (*Pinus sylvestris*). Widespread but extremely local in England and Wales and the only *Sympherobius* species so far recorded in Scotland.

Sympherobius (Niremberge) pellucidus (Walker, 1853)
Extremely local but locally abundant in England and Wales, south of a line from Liverpool to the Humber. Adults have been found in association with both Scots pine and oak.

Sympherobius (Sympherobius) pygmaeus (Rambur, 1842)
Like the preceding species, this insect is extremely local but locally abundant in England and Wales, south of a line from Liverpool to the Humber. Adults have been found in association with both Scots pine and oak.

Wesmaelius (Kimminsia) balticus (Tjeder, 1931)
A coastal species, recorded at only eleven sites from the Severn Estuary to Elgin, via the south coast, with isolated inland records in Wales during the hot summer of 1976. The larvae are associated with aphids specific to marram grass (*Ammophila arenaria*) on stable dune systems. Adults fold their wings and drop to the ground when disturbed (eg. by a sweep net) but they come to light traps readily. Confusion is possible with *Hemerobius micans* which looks similar to the unaided eye, and coastal examples of this latter species should always be examined carefully. It may be under-recorded.

Wesmaelius (Wesmaelius) concinnus (Stephens, 1836)
Widespread and fairly frequent wherever there are Scots pine trees in England and north Wales, but curiously not recorded from central and southern Wales, the West Country, Ireland or the Channel Islands, whilst there are only two known records from Scotland. It is easily beaten from scots pine branches, when it falls to the ground looking deceptively like a falling leaf (one has to be aware that leaves of this shape are not present on pine trees!).

Wesmaelius (Kimminsia) malladai (Navá, 1925)
Restricted in Britain to the Scottish Highlands, where it is local, but often common. This is the *Boriomyia mortoni* of Killington's Monograph (Killington, 1937) and the *Kimminsia killingtoni* of Fraser (1959). Those keys are inadequate for the separation of this species from *W. mortoni* and should not be used.

Wesmaelius (Kimminsia) mortoni (McLachlan, 1899)
Only known in Britain from three specimens from Scotland, but not recorded since 1898 and now almost certainly extinct. Any records will certainly require expert confirmation.

Wesmaelius (Kimminsia) nervosus (Fabricius, 1793)
This is the correct name for the species we have so far called *W. betulinus* in Britain. It is widespread and common throughout the British Isles, especially in Scotland where it replaces *W. subnebulosus* in many areas. Typical forms have variegated wings but there is also a unicolourous form *melancholica* Killington which is identical to the form *melancholica* of *W. subnebulosus*. The two can not be separated 'by eye' in any of their forms.

Wesmaelius (Wesmaelius) quadrifasciatus (Reuter, 1894)
Locally common in England, North Wales and central Scotland, with a single record from eastern Ireland. It is strictly associated with larch (*Larix decidua*) in woodland, but can sometimes be dislodged from adjacent trees of different species.

Wesmaelius (Kimminsia) ravus (Withycombe, 1923)
Extremely local and rare in Surrey, Kent and Hampshire, with an isolated record from a light trap at Bangor, North Wales in 1980 and another from a light trap in Wolverhampton in 1994. It is confined to Scots pine and evidently lives at the very tops of the trees; it is thus likely to be under-recorded. Freshly emerged adults from pupae in litter at the tree base are said to walk immediately up the trunk, this taking place at around 7.30 in the morning during May!

Wesmaelius (Kimminsia) subnebulosus (Stephens, 1836)
Widespread and common throughout the British Isles, and probably our commonest brown lacewing. However, it becomes more localised in Scotland and is replaced by *W. nervosus* in several areas. The unicolourous form *melancholica* Killington is very frequent, especially in urban areas.

MYRMELEONTIDAE – THE ANT LIONS

Euroleon nostras (Fourcro, 1785)
Known from the Channel Islands and from a wide area of the Suffolk sandlings. It is possible (though now rather unlikely) that other species of ant-lion will be found in Britain. However, *Euroleon nostras* is distinctive and additional species will be readily spotted, even if they can't immediately be named. Larvae construct cone-shaped pits in soft, dry sand and live below, feeding on insects that fall in. The adults may be mistaken for damselflies, all brown coloured examples of which seen in sandy soil areas should be captured and examined! The clubbed antennae render ant lions quite distinctive.

OSMYLIDAE – THE GIANT LACEWINGS

Osmylus fulvicephalus (Scopoli, 1763)
Widespread and common in suitable habitat in southern England and throughout Wales, but rather local elsewhere, extending north to central Scotland and recorded in several Irish localities. Adults are best found by day when they rest under horizontal surfaces over or near water, such as bridges or fallen trees. Occasionally taken in light traps or malaise traps. Flies mainly during May and June, especially at dusk. The larvae are amphibious, living amongst mosses in the splash zone of stony streams and capable of surviving total immersion.

SISYRIDAE – THE SPONGE FLIES

Sponge flies are associated, as larvae, with freshwater sponges, and reside within the tissue of the sponge.

Sisyra dalii McLachlan, 1866
Extremely local and scarce in England and Wales. There is an old record from Galway in Ireland but it is not recorded in Scotland or the Channel Islands. Most records are from rock-strewn, fast-flowing upland rivers but it is also recorded from the slower and calcareous River Mole in Surrey. Host sponge species are unrecorded.

Sisyra fuscata (Fabricius, 1793)
Widespread and common throughout the British Isles in association with static or slow flowing water. Host sponges recorded are *Spongilla lacustris* and *Ephydatia fluviatilis*.

Sisyra terminalis Curtis, 1854
Evidently our rarest sponge fly, recorded sparingly from southern England, the Welsh borders and southern Ireland. It appears to favour streams that are overhung by trees.

MECOPTERA

Two British families, as follows:

BOREIDAE

Boreus hyemalis (Linnaeus, 1767) – the snow flea
This species is strongly sexually dimorphic. The female has vestigial wings, but those of the male are modified as spines, serrated on the inner edge, to support the female who sits on his back during mating. It is widely distributed throughout Britain, but so far unrecorded from Ireland. The snow-flea is unique in being mature during winter. It is active from October to April, with a peak of activity in November and December when it can be seen walking across snow-covered ground, especially in upland areas. It is most easily captured in pitfall traps set amongst mosses growing on the ground, or by sorting through mosses in the comfort of a warm kitchen during the Christmas break!

PANORPIDAE – THE SCORPION FLIES

Panorpa cognata Rambur, 1842
This is the least frequently recorded of the three known British scorpion flies, and it is evidently rather local, being recorded from England and Wales, with a single record from Glen Cally, Angus in Scotland. It is evidently absent from Ireland and the Channel Islands. Evidence suggests that it may prefer a calcareous environment.

Panorpa communis Linnaeus, 1758
Widespread and abundant in England and Wales but local and rare in Scotland where it is largely replaced by *P. germanica*. Not recorded for Ireland. Dense vegetation, especially with brambles, is the favoured habitat. When disturbed it folds its wings and drops, so is most easily taken from bushes by placing a net below and shaking the bush gently.

Panorpa germanica Linnaeus, 1758
Widespread and very common in Britain with isolated records in the south of Ireland. In Scotland it replaces *P. communis* in most areas. In Scotland and Ireland, the form *borealis* Stephens, which has no spots on its wings, can be found.

APPENDIX 2

COLLECTING AND PRESERVING LACEWINGS

Sadly, with a few exceptions it is not possible to identify the majority of British lacewings in the field, and it is necessary to collect voucher specimens for later examination under the microscope, though as experience is gained, the number of species requiring retention will reduce and it will become possible to carry out ecological studies without the need to collect. As with all collecting in these more enlightened days, however, it should be conducted with a little thought and consideration and specimens should always be properly labelled, recorded and preserved – never discarded. Bulk sampling methods such as malaise trapping and insecticidal fogging kill huge numbers of insects of all kinds. Neither method is justified, in my view, by the amateur who is only interested in lacewings; such activities should only be carried out as part of a proper survey encompassing several other entomological groups or as a part of a well-planned and adequately-financed research programme. Collecting of individual lacewing specimens, on the other hand, does no harm to populations, even of rare species, and the information gleaned can be a positive asset in the overall conservation effort.

The use of cyanide (including crushed laurel leaves) and ammonia should be avoided for the green lacewings as this affects colours, though brown species do not seem to be adversely affected. The ideal method, if available, is to place the tubes containing the specimens in a deep-freeze for a couple of hours. This seems perhaps the most natural way, in any case; all one is doing is bringing forward the winter a little. Make sure that specimens are fully thawed before handling, or legs and antennae will break off. If a deep-freeze is not available, a small piece of tissue dampened (not soaked) with ethyl acetate and trapped in the top of the tube by the lid, will knock lacewings down almost immediately and kill them within twenty minutes. Green lacewings should not be left in ethyl acetate fumes for too long or they will discolour to yellow. Make sure that you use glass tubes; ethyl acetate 'melts' plastic. If all else fails, a puff of cigarette or cigar smoke into the specimen tube will kill most insects almost immediately by nicotine poisoning (another reminder to give up smoking). However, specimens should be removed to a fresh tube soon afterwards or the tar in the smoke will condense on them. Tubes used in this way will be rendered lethal to any insect subsequently added to them for several days if the top is kept securely in place.

It is a matter of personal preference whether or not lacewings are pinned and 'set' or preserved in a fluid medium such as alcohol. I personally prefer the former for all except the Coniopterygidae, as setting allows venation and other characters to be seen more clearly whilst colours are not distorted by the long term effects of storage in alcohol. I exempt the tiny coniopterygids simply because they are so small that I prefer to clear the entire specimen in order to view the genitalia, rather than to try and detach their abdomens. I also found, after several years of professional experience as a museum biologist, that genitalia collections invariably become separated from the parent collection of pinned insects, and any steps that can be taken to minimise the chance of this happening are to be welcomed.

Setting lacewings is relatively easy. Blocks of plastozote (expanded polyethylene) make ideal setting boards. Cut a groove in the block with a razor blade, Kraft knife or similar, to receive the abdomen of the insect. When pinning, it is advisable to use a headless 'micro' pin (size A2 or A3 is best for all except *Osmylus* and *Euroleon* for which size D3 should be used). Always use stainless steel pins; never use brass under any circumstance as it corrodes rapidly giving rise to a blue-green growth called 'verdigris' that will eventually destroy the specimen. This should be pushed vertically through the thorax, between the wing bases, from above so that a good length of pin protrudes below the insect. This is then placed in the groove cut in the setting block. Open the insect's wings by blowing or with a mounted needle and then push the pin into the groove until the wings are lying flat on the surface. If the wings do not lie flat, remove the pin and insect from the block and try again at a slightly different angle. Once the wings rest flat on the surface they can be held out with four more micro pins. Arrange the antennae parallel to the leading edge of the wing (in some European species the relative lengths of wing and antenna are important) and then hold down wings and antennae with tracing paper strips cut to size and secured with pins. Remove the four micro pins from the wings now, before the insect has dried. Leave it at ordinary room temperature for three or four days and it is ready to be staged and labelled.

Staging is a simple process and allows for safe and easy handling of the specimen. Cut a strip of plastozote about 3 or 4 mm square and about 5 mm longer than the specimen. A long, stainless steel pin (I prefer Continental length size 3 pins with heads) is placed through one end and the specimen is then pinned onto this stage. Labels may now be added to the longer, stouter pin.

Whether you are an entomologist, ecologist or general naturalist, proper labelling of your specimens is a fundamental requirement. An unlabelled specimen is scientifically useless and may as well be discarded without further ado. Labels should be written on rigid paper or thin card using permanent black ink. Coloured paper or card may be used (I use a different colour for lacewings from different countries) but if you are preserving in fluid, test for long-term colour fastness first.

If pinning specimens, you should ideally use acid-free paper or card; it is a little more expensive but, again from museum experience, it is frightening to see pins, in specimens not even 100 years old, completely corroded through by the acid content of the paper used for labelling. Similarly, never ever use a biro to write labels; the acid content of biro ink will dissolve away the label inside 50 years, perhaps less, and will in any case fade to illegibility. Similarly, you should never use photocopied or photographically produced labels, as these too will not last the course. There are even suggestions, now, that labels produced on modern bubble jet or inkjet printers attached to word processors are less than permanent. It may be a drag, but good, old-fashioned hand-written labels in Indian ink are the only proven safe method. Labels should bear the name of the vice-county and the locality of capture, together with capture date and the collector's name as a minimum. Optional extras include a grid reference, habitat data and other information, such as capture method. The identity of the insect, together with the name of the identifier, should also be added. If the identification is subsequently corrected, the original incorrect label should always be kept with the specimen. This sounds strange, but it is a very helpful and long-established practice. In writing these keys, for example, I have found other people's mistakes a valuable source of information and it has enabled me to identify sources of confusion.

For fluid preserved specimens, it is traditional to place all the data on a single label. This should be separated in the fluid from the specimen by a cotton wool bung (Fig. 170) to minimise damage. If alcohol or other volatile preservatives are used, the tubes should be stored upside down in larger jars of the same preservative, as shown in Fig. 171. For pinned material, data labels are traditionally cut to a small size so that viewing the insect is not impeded. This usually means that more than one label is required. Usually, the locality data and date go on the upper label, together with the collector's name; habitat and capture data go on the second label and below that the name of the insect and its identifier. This leaves enough space for additional labelling if the identification is subsequently altered. Once labels are on the pin, they should never be removed as there is a danger of labels getting mixed up and returned to the wrong specimen. Extra pin holes in labels on museum specimens always give cause for concern, especially if the data is in any way out of the ordinary.

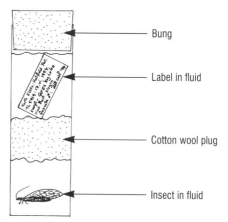

Bung

Label in fluid

Cotton wool plug

Insect in fluid

Fig 170

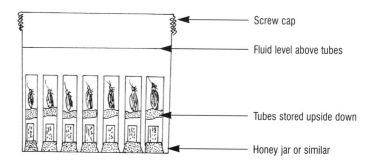

Screw cap

Fluid level above tubes

Tubes stored upside down

Honey jar or similar

Fig 171

APPENDIX 3

PREPARING LACEWING GENITALIA FOR EXAMINATION

Mere mention of 'genitalia' seems to send a great many amateur entomologists into the depths of despair, specimens being placed in boxes for 'experts' to examine, or else ignored for evermore. This is a quite illogical reaction; in many cases examination of the genitalia simply means looking at the shape of the tip of the abdomen! Even when the abdomen needs to be 'cleared' there should be no reason for dismay as it is an extremely easy process that can be done between dinner and watching the news on television!

Materials required:
1. Potassium hydroxide (caustic potash). This can be purchased from most chemists or from hardware shops. If all else fails, dissolve oven cleaner in water and use the liquid (leave any solids that remain behind).
2. A small glass specimen tube.
3. A small saucepan.
4. A kettle.
5. A pair of fine scissors (optional), a small paint brush and a pair of fine forceps.
6. A shallow tray (preferably white, but this is not vital) in which to place the genitalia under the microscope. The lid of a jam jar, or a small saucer will do nicely.
7. Your usual microscope.

Preparing the chemicals: You need to make the potassium hydroxide up to about a ten percent solution in tap water. Ten grammes of potassium hydroxide in 100 mls of water is about right. For safety reasons, always use COLD water and always add the powder/crystals to the water, not the other way round. TIP – if you are not able to weigh 10 grammes, check the total weight of the contents of your new jar of potassium hydroxide and divide the contents into the appropriate number of equal sized portions. For example, if you have a 250 gm jar, make 25 equal piles on a suitable work surface. Remember however, that potassium hydroxide is caustic; it dissolves paper, clothes and fingers in both solid state and solution!

How to prepare specimens for examination: Frequently, specimens preserved in alcohol need no preparation as the features are visible. However, this is not always the case, and in such cases, as well as with all pinned specimens, it will be necessary to render the abdomen translucent, a process called 'clearing'. Detach the abdomen either by snipping with a fine pair of dissecting scissors or by bending it upwards so that it snaps off. TIP – whilst detaching the abdomen hold it with fine forceps wetted with saliva or support it above (if snapping it off) with a paint brush similarly moistened. This will prevent it flying across the room never to be seen again. For the Coniopterygidae, I personally prefer to clear the entire specimen, rather than try to detach and then store the tiny abdomen. Pinned Coniopterygids can easily have the pin withdrawn after treatment.

Doing the deed: Put some potassium hydroxide solution in the specimen tube (about 5 mm is deep is enough) and add the detached abdomen. Place the tube in a saucepan and support it upright. Add boiling water from the kettle to the saucepan to about a centimetre below the top of the tube. Wait about 30 minutes (if this sounds too complicated, abdomens can be left overnight in cold potassium hydroxide solution. Remove the cleared abdomen and place it on the shallow tray. Add some water and gently squash the abdomen with the brush to squeeze out the dissolved contents of the abdomen. Spend some time doing this and look at it under the microscope whilst you do it so you can tell when it is clean. Change the water and examine the abdomen under the microscope. Take care not to detach the genitalia from the abdomen. TIP – if you are looking at several specimens get them all out of the hydroxide and into water before you start squashing them as they may dissolve completely if left for too long.

Finding the genitalia: In most cases you need do almost nothing as the genitalia will be easily visible through the abdomen. Arrange the specimen 'head to left' to interpret the illustrations with this key unless the required view is from below (*Helicoconis* species) or caudal ('tail-on' view with head aligned away from observer) as with *Conwentzia* species. For female scorpion flies (*Panorpa* species), however, you will occasionally need to extract the ovipositor to get a better view, though in a properly cleared specimen it is usually sufficiently visible through the wall of the abdomen. The tip of the abdomen in these specimens has an opening. Pull the top and bottom of the abdomen apart vertically by inserting fine forceps into this opening or, alternatively, use fine scissors to cut along the side of the abdomen. The ovipositor is then grasped with forceps and gently pulled out taking care not to detach it completely.

Preserving the genitalia: Change the water again and leave for half an hour to ensure that all the hydroxide is washed out. You now have a choice. The abdomen can now be removed and glued to a small portion of white card and attached to the same pin as the specimen. Always use water-soluble glue with a fungicide added (wallpaper paste is adequate). This is perfectly acceptable and is my preferred method for material that will not need to be referred to constantly. If you want to preserve the abdomen wet, so that it can be examined frequently with greater ease, you need, perversely, to 'dry' the specimens. Change the water again and then add to it an equal volume of alcohol. After one minute add half as much alcohol again. After a further minute remove the dilute alcohol and replace with pure alcohol. After about 30 seconds the specimen can be removed and stored in a small glass tube of glycerol, which is then corked and added to the same pin as the insect (angled downwards so the glycerol does not leak out). It is not recommended that microscope slides are made, as this inevitably distorts the genitalia and prohibits 3-dimensional viewing.

APPENDIX 4

COMMENTS ON NOMENCLATURE OF LACEWINGS

Linnaeus lumped snake flies, alder flies, true lacewings and scorpion flies together, along with the dragonflies, stoneflies, caddis flies and others, in a single order which he called Neuroptera – a name derived from the Greek and meaning literally 'vein wings'. The true Neuroptera were placed in the sub-order Planipennia. This idea was revised by later workers, who raised the Odonata, Plecoptera, Trichoptera and Mecoptera to order status and retained only the true lacewings (as sub-Order Planipennia) and the snake flies and the alder flies (together in sub-order Megaloptera) in the new order Neuroptera. This remained the accepted classification until quite recently, and these names will be frequently encountered in the literature. Recent thinking, however, is that there are such profound differences between the three groups (particularly the larvae), that all warrant elevation to order status.

Further confusion has arisen from the steadfast opinion of many British workers that all the green coloured 'green lacewings' should be placed in the single genus *Chrysopa*, in spite of a more rapid progress on the continent (eg., Aspöck *et al*, 1980). The old name *Chrysopa* is now split up into six genera in Britain. These are *Cunctochrysa*, *Chrysopidia*, *Chrysoperla*, *Nineta*, *Dichochrysa* and *Chrysopa* sensu stricto. The name *Dichochrysa*, however, is a very recent alteration and may be unfamiliar to many entomologists. It arises from a split of the former genus *Mallada* (=*Anisochrysa*) into two new genera, with all British *Mallada* species so far known being referable to it (Yang & Yang, 1990, 1991).

Other changes have also been made. Earlier British workers regarded *Conwentzia pineticola* as only a form of *C. psociformis*, and *Dichochrysa prasina* as a subspecies of *D. ventralis*; neither view has been shared by workers elsewhere in the world. Numerous other changes have also been made over the years and two new species appear to have colonised Britain, whilst a further four at least have been here quite undetected for well over a hundred years. A further species, *Helicoconis lutea*, once considered to be British, has recently been deleted from the list as it is now known that its presence was based on incorrect identification of other species (Plant, 1991). However, very recently, a female *Helicoconis*, possibly of a different species, has been discovered in the north of Scotland.

The major changes in names are summarised in Table 1, whilst the additions to the British and Irish list are given in Table 2. As a further guide, the reader is referred to the notes on each species included after the keys in Appendix 1. A fully synonymic checklist can be found in Plant (1994), where both generic and specific synonyms are listed in full.

ACKNOWLEDGMENTS

The production of these identification keys has been a slow process over a number of years. Correspondence and discussion with readers of the Neuroptera Recording Scheme newsletter, *Neuro News*, centred very largely upon identification problems and I must, therefore, offer my thanks to these people. I must also thank various museum curators whose collections I have been able to critically examine during the preparation of the keys. In producing keys that work it is necessary to examine as large as possible a sample of the insects that are to be included. The staff of IACR-Rothamsted at Harpenden, Hertfordshire, particularly Adrian Riley and Ian Woiwod, whose nationwide network of light traps provided me with in excess of 30,000 specimens to examine between 1988 and 1995 are also to be mentioned here. Additionally, I must acknowledge the many light trap operators, both professional and amateur, who took the time to provide the samples from the Rothamsted traps.

As far as individuals are concerned, it is also most appropriate to name in particular Dr Howard Mendel of Ipswich Museum, whose initial suggestion it was that I should prepare a key for the AIDGAP series, and both Peter Barnard and Stephen Brooks of the Natural History Museum in London, who have provided me with considerable assistance through discussion and constructive criticism. Peter Barnard has also produced a number of draft keys to lacewings and presented these in *Neuro News*; elements of all these have been incorporated in the keys in this AIDGAP guide; I am indebted to Peter for allowing me to do this. Stephen Brooks also provided particular help in sorting out the problems within the *Chrysoperla carnea* complex. Valuable correspondence has also been had with Professor Horst Aspöck, Dr Ulrike Aspöck and Herbert Hölzel in Austria, who have been kind enough to offer me second opinions on specimens that were a potential problem.

I must mention the army of 'testers' who received the draft version of these keys and offered a large number of extremely helpful comments and criticisms which enabled me to improve the final version considerably, including a complete rewrite of some parts. Also Mark Dowding for the cover design.

Finally, my most grateful thanks go to Dr Steve Tilling, the Publications Manager for the Field Studies Council, who has overseen the whole project, coordinated the testing of the draft keys, sorted, compiled and passed to me the comments of all the testers and assisted me greatly in his editorial capacity.

I hope that with all of this assistance, the keys will now prove a workable addition to the identification literature for British insects. However, they are unlikely to be perfect and I would be most pleased to have the opportunity to examine any specimen that can not be run smoothly through the keys.

REFERENCES

ASPÖCK, H., ASPÖCK, U. and HÖLZEL, (1980). *Die Neuropteren Europas* (vols. 1 & 2). Krefeld: Goecke & Evers.

ASPÖCK, H., ASPÖCK, U. and RAUSCH, H., (1991). *Die Raphidiopteren der Erde* (vols. 1 & 2). Krefeld: Goecke & Evers.

BARNARD, P. C., (1977). *Sialis nigripes* Pictet (Megaloptera: Sialidae), an alder fly new to Britain and Ireland. *Entomologist's Gazette* **28**: 269-274.

BARNARD, P. C., (1978). A Check-list of the British Neuroptera with taxonomic notes. *Entomologist's Gazette*, **29**, 165-176.

BARNARD, P. C., BROOKS, S. J. and STORK, N. E., (1986). The seasonality and distribution of Neuroptera, Raphidioptera and Mecoptera on oaks in Richmond Park, Surrey, as revealed by insecticide knock-down sampling. *Journal of Natural History*, **20**, 1321-1331.

BROOKS, S. J., (1994). A taxonomic review of the common green lacewing genus *Chrysoperla* (Neuroptera: Chrysopidae). *Bulletin of the Natural History Museum (Entomology)*, **63**(2), 137-210

BROOKS, S. J. and BARNARD, P. C., (1990). The green lacewings of the world: a generic review. *Bulletin of the British Museum (Natural History), (Entomology)*, **59**, 117-286.

FRASER, F. C., (1959). *Mecoptera, Megaloptera and Neuroptera.* Handbooks for the Identification of British Insects 1 (12 & 13): 1-40.

GÜNTHER, K. K., (1993). Welche Art muss *Coniopteryx pygmaea* Enderlein, 1906 heißen? *Deutsche entomologische Zeitschrift*, **40**, 167-171.

HOLLIER, J. A. and BELSHAW, R. D., (1993). Stratification and phenology of a woodland Neuroptera assemblage. *Entomologist*, **112**, 169-175.

HYND, W. R. B., (1989). *Coniopteryx lentiae* Aspöck & Aspöck (Neuroptera: Coniopterygidae) new to Britain. *Entomologist's Gazette*, **40**, 149-150.

HYND, W. R. B. and PLANT, C. W., (1991). *Coniopteryx esbenpeterseni* Tjeder, 1930 (Neuroptera: Coniopterygidae) new to Britain with a comment on the subgenus *Metaconiopteryx* in Britain. *Entomologist's Gazette*, **42**, 104-106.

KILLINGTON, F. J., (1936, 1937). *A Monograph of the British Neuroptera.* London: Ray Society.

LERAUT, P., (1991). Les *Chrysoperla* de la faune de France *Entomologica gallica*, **2**, 75-81.

LERAUT, P., (1992) Névroptères des Alpes centrales Françaises (Neur.) *Entomologica gallica*, **3**, 59-65.

MENDEL, H., (1996). *Euroleon nostras* (Fourcroy, 1785) a British species and notes on ant-lions (Neuroptera Myrmeleontidae) in Britain. *Entomologist's Record and Journal of Variation*, **108**, 1-5.

PLANT, C. W., (1991). An introduction to the British wax flies (Neuroptera: Coniopterygidae) with a revised key to British species. *British Journal of Entomology and Natural History*, **4**, 99-117.

PLANT, C. W., (1992). *Semidalis pseudouncinata* Meinander, 1963 (Neuroptera: Coniopterygidae) new to Britain with a note on its separation from *S. aleyrodiformis* (Stephens). *Entomologist's Gazette*, **43**, 292-296.

PLANT, C. W., (1993). *Cunctochrysa bellifontensis* Leraut, 1988 (Neuroptera: Chrysopidae), a lacewing new to Britain, with a note on its identification. *Entomologist's Gazette*, **44**, 41-44.

PLANT, C. W., (1994). *Provisional atlas of the lacewings and allied insects (Neuroptera, Megaloptera, Raphidioptera and Mecoptera) of Britain and Ireland.* Biological Records Centre: Huntingdon.

PLANT, C. W., (1996). *Nineta inpunctata* (Reuter, 1894) (Neuoroptera: Chrysopidae): a new lacewing recorded in Britain. *Entomologist's Gazette*, **47**, 115-120.

PLANT, C. W. and BARNARD, P. C., (1988). *Hemerobius fenestratus* Tjeder (Neuroptera: Hemerobiidae) new to Britain. *Entomologist's Gazette*, **39**, 292.

WARD L. K., (1970). *Aleuropteryx juniperi* ohm (Neur.: Coniopterygidae) new to Britain feeding on *Carulaspis juniperi* Bouché (Hem.: Diaspididae). *Entomologist's Monthly Magazine*, **106**, 74-78.

YANG, X.-K. and YANG, C.-K., (1990). *Navasius*, a new genus of Chrysopinae (Neuroptera: Chrysopidae). *Acta Zootaxonomica Sinica*, **15**(3), 327-338.

YANG, X.-K. and YANG, C.-K., (1991). *Dichochrysa* nom. nov. for *Navasius* Yang & Yang, 1990 (Neuroptera: Chrysopidae) *nec* Esben-Petersen (Neuroptera: Myrmeleonidae). *Scientific Treatese on Systematic and Evolutionary Biology*, **1**, 150.

The AIDGAP Publications

The following AIDGAP titles have been published by the Field Studies Council

A key to the adults of British lacewings and their allies Colin Plant (1997)

A key to the major groups of marine invertebrates John Crothers (1997)

A field key to the shore fishes of the British Isles Alwyne Wheeler (1994)

Random-access identification guides for a microcomputer (includes a sedges database) Available in BBC and IBM formats, Colin Legg (1992)

The Fern Guide: an introductory guide to the ferns, clubmosses, quillworts and horsetails of the British Isles James Merryweather & Michael Hill (1992)

A field guide to the sharks of British coastal waters Philip Vas (1991)

A key to the woodlice of Britain and Ireland Stephen Hopkin (1991)

Insects of the British cow-dung community Peter Skidmore (1991)

British Sawflies (Hymenoptera: Symphyta): a key to adults of the genera occurring in Britain Adam Wright (1990)

Soil Types: a field identification guide Stephen Trudgill (1989)

Keys to the families of British Spiders Lawrence Jones-Walters (1989)

A key to adults of British Water Beetles L.E. Friday (1988)

A key to the major groups of British Terrestrial Invertebrates S.M. Tilling (1987)

A key to the major groups of British Freshwater Invertebrates P.S. Croft (1986)

Sea Spiders. A revised key to the adults of littoral Pycnogonida in the British Isles Phil King (1986)

A field guide to the British Red Seaweeds (Rhodophyta) Sue Hiscock (1986)

British Grasses, a punched-card key to Grasses in the vegetative state Richard Pankhurst & Judith Allinson (1985)

Bees, Ants & Wasps – the British Aculeates Pat Willmer (1985)

A key to the families of British Coleoptera (beetles) and Strepsiptera Dennis Unwin (1984: revised 1988)

A field guide to the Slugs of the British Isles R.A.D. Cameron, B. Eversham & N. Jackson (1983) OUT OF PRINT

A key to the Crabs and Crab-like Animals of British inshore waters John & Marilyn Crothers (1983: revised 1988)

A key to families of British Diptera Dennis Unwin (1981)

An illustrated guide to the Diatoms of British coastal plankton J.B. Sykes (1981)

A Field key to the British Brown Seaweeds Sue Hiscock (1979) OUT OF PRINT

These, and many other FSC titles, may be purchased when visiting Field Studies Council Centres or may be ordered through the post from:
FSC Publications, Field Studies Council, Preston Montford, Shrewsbury SY4 1HW Tel: 01743 850370 • Fax: 01743 850178

A complete list of titles and prices is also available from this address.